LIFE AND HEALTH

IN

THREE PALESTINIAN VILLAGES

Rita Giacaman
Community Health Unit
Birzeit University

Photographs by Emile Ashrawi

Ithaca Press
London & Atlantic Highlands
1988

Jerusalem Studies Series No 14

First published in 1988
by Ithaca Press 13 Southwark Street London SE 1 1RQ
& 171 First Avenue Atlantic Highlands NJ 07716

Printed & bound in England
by Biddles Ltd Guildford & King's Lynn

British Library Cataloguing in Publication Data
Giacamon, Rita
  Life and Health in three Palestinian Villages. - (Jerusalem
  Studies Series; v.14).

  1. Medical economics—West Bank 2.Social medicine—West Bank
  3. Palestinian Arabs—Health and hygiene—West Bank
  I.Title II.Series
  362.1'042'095695 RA410.55.J6

  ISBN 0 86372 086 2
  ISBN 0 86372 087 0 Pbk

Library of Congress Cataloging-in-Publication Data
Giacaman, Rita
    (Jerusalem Studies Series; no. 14
    Bibliography: p.
    1.Public health--West Bank. 2.Public health--Gaza Strip.
3.Women--Health and hygiene--West Bank. 4.Children--Health and
hygiene--West Bank. 5.Children--Health and hygiene--Gaza Strip.
6. Children--Health and hygiene--Gaza Strip. I.Title. II. Series
RA541.W47G53 1988   362.1'095695   87-3806
ISBN 0-86372-086-2
ISBN 0-86372-087-0 (pbk.)

CONTENTS

TABLES AND CHARTS

Photographs on pages 87-92

APPENDICES

ACKNOWLEDGEMENTS

There are many people I would like to thank for the support that made the completion of this study possible. On the West Bank, I would like to particularly thank Iman Masri, Mohammad Said, Hala Salem and Lo'ai Kamhieh - the members of the research team - for their diligence and commitment to the project. To Judy Blanc and Charles Kamen, consultant social scientists to the project, I owe thanks for insights and moral support when the frustration levels were high. I would also like to thank the staff of the Community Health Unit for their willingness to share my workload during the academic year 1984-85, when I was completing the analysis of this study in England. My gratitude also goes to George Giacaman, Vera Tamari, Lisa Taraki and Chris Smith for their unconditional support throughout the period when I was working on this study, and for thought provoking comments. To Mustafa Barghouthi and the Union of Palestinian Medical Relief Committees I would like to extend my deep appreciation for providing the institutional framework and context through which academic work could become meaningful.

On the English end, I would like to thank Sarah Graham-Brown, Elfi Pallis, Maxine Molyneux, Allison Scott, Harold Wolpe, C. B. Winsten, David Rose, Nicky Hart, and Eric Tannenbaum for valuable comments and support. To the friends at South Street, Colchester, where I lived for part of the academic year, I owe many insights that came in the course of casual discussion. I also owe them, and especially Laura Corballis, thanks for general support. Thanks also go to Beth Goldring and Tina Schmalenach for editorial assistance. Finally, I would like to thank the Population Council, Cairo, Egypt and the International Development Research Centre, Ottawa, Canada, for financial assistance.

INTRODUCTION

This study attempts to contribute to the understanding of health
and its determinants in the Israeli-occupied West Bank and Gaza
Strip. Its primary purpose is to elaborate, through a systematic
discussion of health conditions in three Palestinian villages,
the problems and biases inherent in the way in which Palestinians
conceive of and deal with health in the area in general. It is
intended to raise fundamental questions pertaining to the
internal Palestinian debate on health and not to account for the
major effects the conditions of Israeli military occupation have
on people's health, indeed, daily life. For this reason I shall
touch on the effects of occupation minimally and only when it is
necessary to do so to illuminate points pertaining to internally
generated conflicts and health problems. The study was conceived
and executed at a time when the hopes and aspirations of
Palestinians for nationhood, a state, a political identity - in
short, a decent life - were continually being frustrated by local
and international events. At that time, although the Palestinian
question was receiving worldwide attention to the extent that the
existence and the problems of about four million people could not
longer be ignored, little was known of the effects of military
occupation on specific aspects of daily life. While a significant amount of research was being generated on such issues as
land confiscation; violations of human rights and international
agreements; the building of settlements; and the impact of
colonial policies on the Palestinian economy and social structure (1), hardly anything beyond generalised arguments had been
written on the impact of these transformations on health. On the
one hand, the Israeli military government attempted to convince
the world, and the Palestinians as well, that everyone ought to
be thankful for Israeli colonization of the area since it had
brought modernity and improved health standards to the region
(2). On the other hand, Palestinians were responding to these
allegations with counter-assertions that the health status of the
occupied population was deteriorating (3). By the late 1970s, it
had become apparent that Israeli military government statistics
were at least inadequate; and represented a substantial underestimation of real trends. A case in point was the effort to
estimate infant mortality rates for the area: research by both
Palestinians and Israelis was yielding estimates of around 80
deaths/1000 live births for the West Bank in the 1975-77 period
(4); while the military government was still producing figures
in the range of 28-30/1000 (5).

The Palestinians, however, remained in a weak position with regard to the argument over health, for several impediments hindered the development of more detailed and accurate assessments. To begin with, even the minimal public sector records on health and social services were not generally accessible to Palestinian researchers. One had to resort to rather unorthodox methods of data collection; sometimes via a visiting international delegation, or through foreign visitors thought of as important by the Israeli military. Even visits to public sector hospitals and clinics staffed by Palestinians, but controlled by the military proved to be a dead end on most occasions. The orders were strict and clear: Absolutely no information was to be provided without the prior permission of the Israeli military authorities. This left the private sector as the only source of information; but its general state of disorganisation offered few possibilities for concrete and reliable information-gathering. Permission to conduct national health surveys was refused (6). These factors, coupled with the general inadequacy of research facilities in the region, reduced research efforts to a minimum, which concentrated on noting and exposing general deterioration in the health services infrastructure. The lack of other types of data, in addition to the documentable deterioration in the level of services provided (7), led to the conflation of arguments about the neglect of health services by the military government with those about the general health status of the population. In the late 1970s Palestinian health researchers were arguing about the deterioration of health conditions of Palestinians living under occupation based on studies conducted almost entirely on health services. The ongoing debate was structured and restricted by a biomedical, as opposed to a social, conception of health and disease. This, in turn, led to the conflation of two interconnected but nonetheless separate phenomena: health conditions and health services, which became interchangeable in discussion, writing and political debate.

By the late 1970s and early 1980s, the general rediscovery of rural areas by various groups involved in development work in the West Bank was accompanied by new attempts to institute development projects at the village level. With these attempts came a new genre of health research; one that entailed examining the details and specifics of the health conditions which were to form the foundation upon which health projects could be based (8). Through these micro-level studies, as well as others that dealt with the effects of military occupation on the economy and social structure at the village level, came the slow realization that the health picture was actually more complex than was once assumed. It became clear that health services and health levels did not necessarily follow the same trends. More importantly perhaps, a combination of tentative health data and simple observations led researchers to suspect that health conditions in the different regions of the occupied territories did not altogether conform to the prevailing and generalised argument on health that Palestinians had presented. While in some regions health conditions were found to be much worse than was previously believed, in others it appeared as if the trend were one of

improvement.   Thus the re-establishment of contacts with the
village led to the process of questioning assumptions, and re-
evaluating perspectives and approaches in health research.   This
study is one manifestation of this new collective consciousness.

As Germaine Tillion once expressed it, the study belongs to a
'scientific no-man's-land' (9), on the margins of the medical
sciences, sociology, anthropology and demography.   With a wave of
scientifism growing in the occupied territories, this wider and
more extensive view of health may provoke some criticism.   A
growing understanding of the nature of health, however, dictates
an approach that incorporates wider issues, and therefore a break
with the biomedical paradigm.   Since it is intended to contribute
to the internal Palestinian debate on health, this study
emphasises what Palestinians do or do not do, as opposed to
concentrating on the further incrimination of Israeli military
rule.   It is guided by the need to re-examine the ways in which
Palestinians respond to the effects of colonization.   The
investigation of health problems in three Palestinian villages
was thought to be an appropriate medium through which to raise
questions regarding the present Palestinian modes of thinking and
of operation; and possibly to contribute in a very small way to a
people's struggle for liberation from all forms of exploitation.
Thus, the tone is that of criticism from within.   It exempts no
one, including the author and the progressive movement that the
author believes represents the hope for change.   This study is
dedicated to the women's, medical relief, agricultural relief,
and voluntary work popular movements; for it is their emergence
as a significant social force and as the primary agency that
could bring about change that provides the primary justification
for this research effort.

A Historical Overview

Since health conditions are a manifestation of socio-economic and
historical phenomena, the study of health cannot be divorced
from the study of colonization.   Throughout its recent history,
Palestinian society has been dominated by the rule of four
foreign regimes: that of the Ottomans; the British; the Jor-
danians; and now the Israelis (10).   In the second half of the
nineteenth century, the processes of economy and social change
included, among other phenomena, the expansion of the cultivated
area, the development of exports, and the growth of population
(11).   But the natural increase of the population appears to have
been modest until the end of Turkish rule.   This suggests that
mortality rates were high for both children and adults, since
fertility changed very little before the 1960s (12).   The advent
of British colonial rule brought further changes.   The policies
pursued by the British in Palestine shared many features with
those pursued by other colonisers, most notably in the spheres of
colonial finance and administration (13).   Capitalist penetration
of the countryside and changes in tenure relations, productive
processes, and labour power all contributed to the development of
market forces (14), and to the probably substantial improvement

in the standard of living. Thus, although expenditure on public
services and social welfare was low (15), a sharp decline in
morbidity and mortality was observed throughout the period of the
British Mandate (16).   The costs of these improvements, however,
were extremely high.   Among other deleterious consequences, they
came in the form of the 1917 Balfour Declaration for the
establishment of a Jewish homeland in Palestine and the creation
of the state of Israel in 1948, with the resulting dispossession
and dispersion of Palestinians, and the dismemberment of their
society.

The shattering experience of the 1948 Arab-Israeli War left
almost 800,000 people homeless and outside the territories on
which the state of Israel was erected.   Refugees fled to the
remaining portions of Western Palestine - the Gaza Strip and the
West Bank - and to neighbouring Arab countries, most notably
Jordan, Syria, and Lebanon (17).   Jordan's 1950 annexation of the
West Bank signalled the beginning of a new period, one perhaps
best characterised by a process of gradual disillusionment with
Arab regimes.   Throughout this period, Palestinians were becoming
increasingly dissatisfied with the policies of the Jordanian
regime, which favoured growth and development in the East Bank at
the expense of the West Bank (18).   Moreover, the experience of
refugee life in the Arab world pointed to the need for Palestinians to play an independent role in the resolution of their
national fate.   In 1964, the Palestine Liberation Organisation
was created, with the blessing of Arab regimes, 'as an envelope
to contain the emerging non-conformity of the Palestinians'(19),
as Ibrahim Dakkak has expressed it.   Despite attempts at
containment, however, the re-opening of discussions among
Palestinians and the rapid re-emergence of Palestinian national
consciousness took root; they proved to be instrumental in the
mobilisation of Palestinians all over the world for national
liberation.

By 1967, and with the fall of the West Bank and Gaza Strip and
their approximately 1.3 million Palestinians under Israeli
military rule, the credibility of Arab regimes was almost
completely lost.   In the mid-1970s it became clear that the
conditions of Israeli occupation were bringing about dramatic
changes, which necessitated new modes of action.   Land confiscation measures; the colonisation of the area by Israeli settlers;
and the Israeli control of water resources, among many other
factors, led the Palestinians to react at more than one level.
The leadership outside the occupied territories mounted its
response through armed struggle for liberation and through
diplomatic means.   Inside the occupied territories, activity
remained largely at political, organisational and institutional
levels.   This failure of military resistance to take root in the
occupied areas (20) may also have been connected to the nature of
the economic transformation of the area and the social changes
that accompanied it.   Though those were much less dramatic than
other changes, they were more insidious and are perhaps more
permanent.   In general terms, 18 years of occupation have reduced
the West Bank and Gaza Strip to a situation of dependence on

Israel in almost every aspect of life. A move away from agriculture as the major source of income among peasant households took place, but was not accompanied by a drift of the rural population to the cities, nor by the development of a fully capitalist commercial agriculture (21). Industry was never highly developed in the area. It continued to suffer from low levels of investment and general stagnation (22), remaining in a primitive state, without the investment necessary for future economic growth (23). What did take place was a process of de-peasantisation, whereby Palestinians moved into wage labour in Israel in search of livelihood. Palestinians became Israel's 'reserve army of labour'. Thus, by 1977, Palestinian employment in Israel (excluding the self-employed) was estimated at about 50 per cent of total employment among the inhabitants of the West Bank and Gaza (24). Generally, their earnings tended to be one third to one half those of Israeli workers (25). Most of these workers were hired on a daily and temporary basis; many illegally, and under inhuman living conditions (26). They thus remained, as is the case today, in a very precarious situation, subject to the fluctuations in market conditions. The precariousness of their situation is a matter of Israeli policy. As Emmanuel Farjoun has noted:

> What the Bank (of Israel) is saying is that in times of depression, when workers must be made redundant, the Israeli economy can avoid the political dangers of mass unemployment by dismissing only the elastic part of the workforce: marginal age-groups (the young and the old) and marginal people, workers from the occupied territories (27).

In spite of all this, individual incomes rose; for employment in Israel succeeded in reducing the previously high level of unemployment to a minimum, and resulted in a generalised increase in the purchasing power of a significant sector of the population (28). In the rural areas, where the economic consequences of the occupation were most markedly felt, the combination of colonial policies and the requirements of Israeli capital manifested themselves in different ways. In the Jordan Valley region, the consequences of occupation were severe and threatened the destruction of village society by the late 1970s (29). By contrast, in regions where land confiscation was minimal, and where agricultural production depended largely on rainfall, work opportunities in Israel resulted in improved incomes and a generally improved standard of living. Moreover, while wage labour did not generate the wealth necessary to induce capitalist investments at the village level, it did contribute to a new homogeneity in village class structure - in the sense that the gap between rich and poor narrowed - and to a reduction of the cleavages in peasant society (30).

While the dearth of information regarding health levels in the West Bank and Gaza Strip in the pre-1967 period makes it impossible to produce reliable time-trend delineations, the initial evidence suggests that infant and child mortality in the

region generally continued to fall, as it had done during the
1950s and 1960s (31).   But the regional variations were substantial, and appear to have been largely due to the impact of
economic changes and colonial policy measures on living conditions and incomes.   The overall rate remains high: even in the
early 1980s, the West Bank infant mortality rate was estimated at
between 50-100 deaths/1000 live births (32).   Inadequate health
conditions, coupled with a generalised deterioration in the
services infrastructure that accompanied military occupation,
prompted Palestinians to mount a development response, which took
the form mainly of provision of services.

By the mid-1970s, Arab money began to pour into the occupied
territories through a number of channels.   One of these, the
Jordan-Palestine Liberation Organisation Joint Committee, was set
up in 1977 to oversee and administer the distribution of money in
the area.   These funds were primarily intended to support the
needs of those who could no longer withstand the effects of
occupation.   To some extent these funds did provide the basis
upon which Palestinian educational and other institutions were
able to survive, even thrive; but the channelling of funds into
the area soon turned into a means for achieving political ends,
and hardly touched the problems of those who needed help most.
It was as if development aims and objectives did not matter.   The
building of constituencies, mostly in the towns and among those
who are politically and economically powerful, and at the expense
of the rural and urban poor, took precedence.

Thus, while initial Palestinian efforts under occupation were
geared toward steadfastness and national unity, they failed to
take into consideration that Palestinian society was not
homogeneous, but was divided along clan, class and gender lines,
and that life under Israeli military rule was governed by more
than the national political contradiction.   This thinking led to
a variety of 'steadfastness' and 'development project' work,
funded at times by large amounts of money from Arab sources.   By
the 1980s, however, it was becoming clear that steadfastness did
not take into consideration divisions and interests in Palestinian society; nor did it take into consideration Palestinian
factionalism, which was led, also, by forces outside the
Palestinian community.   This factionalism, as Dakkak has noted,
'worked to disrupt the unity of the national movement' (33).
Factionalism today is also leading to the disruption of development efforts.

Three Communities

The three highland villages that are the focus of this study are
located in the Ramallah District of the West Bank.   The population is predominantly Sunni Muslim, as is the case with the
majority of West Bank villages.   It is stable and homogeneous in
that the inhabitants have lived there for centuries (34).   A
small refugee community took shelter in one of the villages in
the late 1940s.   However, unlike the situation with most 1948 and

1967 Palestinian refugees, this refugee community has succeeded in integrating into village life; in purchasing land from the local landowners, and in pursuing a lifestyle very similar to that of the original inhabitants.

Until recently, rainfall-dependent agriculture formed the economic base for these communities. The region in general was known for its olive, fruit, and pulse production. The harvest was both used for family consumption and sold in the Ramallah market. Today, however, the majority of men in these villages are employed as wage labourers in the West Bank, Israel, and the Arab Gulf States. The opening-up of opportunities for wage labour after 1967, coupled with such other factors as land fragmentation, contributed to an increasing neglect of the land. The economic and social transformations that accompanied the fall of the West Bank under Israeli military rule imparted their effects on most aspects of life in these communities, and especially on work and consumption patterns.

At the time of the survey, which forms the core of this investigation, the communities appeared to be undergoing a process of rapid change. Thus, in 1981, entry into villages was made possible through contact with the Mukhtars (hamula, or extended family, heads) and a few of the village elders and notables. By 1984 it was also necessary to establish connection with the newly proliferating village youth clubs in order to gain their support and backing and ensure health project success. The shifts in the local centres of power as a result of post-1967 transformations were being felt in the early 1980s. Additionally, although the phenomenon of women wage workers in Israeli enterprises was almost invisible in 1981, by 1984 several cases were in evidence; and it appeared that the incorporation of women into the wage labour market was becoming increasingly accepted by these communities.

The inhabitants were caught between two ways of life: that of peasants and that of proletarians. Those who worked as wage labourers in the West Bank and Israel maintained relatively strong ties with their villages; they were primarily daily commuters. Despite wage work, they continued to participate in the agricultural cycle to some extent and in village life in general. Yet, wage labour incomes, remittances from abroad, and an increasing exposure to the outside world also meant new consumption and living patterns. The abundance of televisions and other electrical gadgets; the use of powdered milk to feed infants; and the decline in the use of women's traditional Palestinian dresses are features which immediately strike the visitor. The standard of living in general was visibly better than that of the poorer Hebron District or Jordan Valley villages, yet lower than that of villages that rely mostly on Gulf remittances for survival. Thus, by West Bank standards, these villages are located around the middle of a rich/poor scale.

Though it would have been useful to attempt delineating changes in the health status of the inhabitants over the past several years, and as a reflection of socio-economic changes, the task proved impossible because of the absence of the relevant database. Because of this, the discussion of health in this study centres around the present, while drawing as much as possible on various sorts of information to at least suggest a historical process. It is hoped that micro-level health studies of this kind, conducted in the various regions of the West Bank, will contribute to building up the database necessary for comparative purposes as well as the delineation of time trends.

NOTES

1. A relatively wide range of literature of this nature exists today. See for instance Shehadeh, R & Kuttab, J, <u>The West Bank and the Rule of Law</u>, International Commission of Jurists/Law in the Service of Man, New York, 1980; Tamari, S, 'The Palestinians in the West Bank and Gaza', in Nakhleh, K & Zureik, E (eds), <u>The Sociology of the Palestinians</u>, Croom Helm, London, 1980; Aruri, N, <u>Occupation Israel Over Palestine</u>, Zed, London, 1984; Farjoun, E, 'Palestinian Workers in Israel: A Reserve Army of Labour', in Rothschild, J (ed), <u>Forbidden Agendas: Intolerance and Defiance in the Middle East</u>, Al-Saqi, London, 1984; Dakkak, I, 'Back to Square One: A Study in the Reemergence of the Palestinian Identity in the West Bank 1967-1980', in Schoelch, A (ed), <u>Palestinians Over the Green Line</u>, Ithaca, London, 1983.

2. See, for instance, <u>Health and Health Services in Judea, Samaria and Gaza</u>, a Report by the Ministry of Health of Israel to the Thirty-Sixth World Health Assembly, Geneva, May 1983. State of Israel, Ministry of Health, Jerusalem, March 1983. A response to this report may be found in Giacaman R, 'Inquiétantes Distorsions: Les Conditions Sanitaires en Cisjordanie, Réponse au rapport du ministre israélien de la Santé publique devant la trente-sixième Assemblé de l'Organisation mondiale de la santé, sur l'état sanitaire et les services de santé dans les territoires occupés, Genève, mai 1983', <u>Revue d'Etudes Palestiniennes</u>, June 1984, pp. 23-26.

3. See Katbeh, S, <u>The Status of Health Services in the West Bank</u>, Jordan Medical Council, Jerusalem, 1977.

4. Ibid, p. 13, and Schmelz, U O, Nathan, G & Kenvin, J, <u>Multiplicity Study of Births and Deaths in Judea, Samaria and Gaza, North Sinai</u>, Technial Publications Series no. 44, Israel Central Bureau of Statistics, Jerusalem, 1977, pp. 75-77.

5. <u>Health and Health Services</u>, op cit, p. 4.

6. Roberts, A, Jorgensen, B & Newman, F, <u>Academic Freedom Under Israeli Military Occupation: Report of WUS/ICJ Mission of Inquiry into Higher Education in the West Bank and Gaza</u>, World University Service/International Commission of Jurists, London/Geneva, 1984, p. 68.

7. Katbeh, op cit; Giacaman, op cit; Benvenisti, M, <u>The West Bank and Gaza Data Base Project: A Pilot Study Report</u>, Jerusalem, 1982, pp. 14-15.

8. Those include a study that was conducted at Bethlehem University under the direction of Thiyab Ayoush and George

De Napoli on Bethlehem District villages at the request of Caritas in 1979, the survey conducted by Alex Pollock of the northern Jordan Valley villages for the Arab Thought Forum, Jerusalem, in 1983-84; and Tamari, S & Giacaman, R, <u>The Social Impact of Drip Irrigation on a Palestinian Peasant Community in the Jordan Valley</u>, Birzeit University, Birzeit, 1980. This study was conducted at the request of the Mennonite Central Committee.

9.   Tillion, G, <u>The Republic of Cousins</u>, Al-Saqi, London, 1983, p. 9.

10. For further information regarding the impact of those regimes on Palestinian economy and society, see Owen, R (ed), <u>Studies in the Economic and Social History of Palestine in the Nineteenth and Twentieth Century</u>, Macmillan, London, 1982; Rodinson, M, <u>Israel: A Colonial Settler State</u>, Mondad, New York, 1973; Zureik, E, <u>The Palestinians in Israel: A Study in Internal Colonialism</u>, Routledge & Kegan Paul, London, 1979; Said, E, <u>The Question of Palestine</u>, Routledge & Kegan Paul, London, 1980.

11. Owen, op cit, p. 2.

12. Hill A, 'The Palestinian Population of the Middle East', <u>Population and Development Review</u>, Vol 9, no 2, June 1983, p. 298.

13. Owen, op cit, p. 4.

14. Graham-Brown, S, 'The Political Economy of Jabal Nablus, 1920-48', in Owen, op cit, pp. 88-176.

15. Ibid, p. 94.

16. Hill, op cit, p. 298.

17. Lesch, A, 'Palestine Land and People', in Aruri, op cit, p. 48.

18. Ibid, pp. 49-50; see also Ma'oz, M, <u>Palestinian Leadership on the West Bank</u>, Frank Cass, London, 1984, pp. 24-59.

19. Dakkak, op cit, p. 68.

20. Ibid, p. 75.

21. Graham-Brown, S, 'The Economic Consequences of Occupation', in Aruri, op cit, p. 191.

22. Ibid, pp. 192-200.

23. Budeiri, M, 'Changes in the Economic Structure of the West Bank and Gaza Strip under Israeli Occupation', Labour, Capital and Society, Vol 15, no 1, April 1982, p. 56.

24. Farjoun, op cit, pp. 98-100.

25. Ibid, p. 118; see also 'In the Factory: Oriental Jews Versus Palestinians', Ha'ir (Friday supplement of Ha'aretz for Tel Aviv), 27.11.81. An English translation is reproduced in Israel Mirror, no 591, 19.1.82.

26. Farjoun, op cit, p. 115; see also 'New Data on Palestinian Workers in Israel', Ha'aretz, 21.2.83, in Israel Mirror, no 637, 2.3.83.

27. Farjoun, op cit, p. 101.

28. Budeiri, op cit, pp. 57-58.

29. See for instance Tamari and Giacaman, op cit; Matar, I, 'Israeli Settlements and Palestinian Rights', in Aruri, op cit, pp. 117-141.

30. Tamari, S, 'Building Other People's Homes: The Palestinian Peasant's Household and Work in Israel', Journal of Palestine Studies, Vol XI, no 1, Autumn 1981, pp. 60-61.

31. Hill, op cit, pp. 302-303.

32. Giacaman, op cit.

33. Dakkak, op cit, p. 88.

34. See al-Dabbagh M, Biladuna Falastin, 2/8, Beirut, 1974, pp. 314-315 and 329-330 (in Arabic); Guerin V, Description Géographique, Historique et Archéologique de la Palestine: Judée, Tome III, Amsterdam, 1969 (reprint of the Paris, 1869 edition), pp. 35-40.

CHAPTER ONE

PROBLEMATIC CONCEPTIONS OF HEALTH

The state of the health debate among Palestinians living both inside and outside the occupied territories is not difficult to summarise. Three basic theoretical formulations for conceiving health and health care can be identified. The first, the biomedical/clinical framework, is generally espoused by the majority of the medical and allied health care establishment. Having been mostly trained in the Western medical tradition, this establishment has been successful in implanting, without modification, a Western medical care system into a society whose health and disease characteristics are radically different from those of the system's point of origin. Moreover, in a society that lacks necessary technological supports for the system, its different components have on numerous occasions appeared as caricatures of their originals (1).

This biomedical framework conceives of health as a purely biological phenomenon; it views the body as a machine. Though the body's parts are seen as interacting, they are nevertheless dealt with as though they functioned separately. The framework views disease as a mechanical malfunction of systems and organs that can be corrected by technical intervention on the part of 'qualified' health care providers. It views the process of medical care and healing in the same mechanical/technical terms. They are thought of as occurring almost solely within the limits of the clinic, the hospital, the laboratory, and the pharmacy. The stethoscope, injections, X-ray machines, drugs, and hospital beds form the core of what is perceived as medical care. Cause and effect relationships embodied in this model are clear-cut and unidimensional. Disease in this framework has a specific etiology (2). If the offending agent is identified, the presence of disease is confirmed; if it is not, the search continues for a specific biological cause. The absence of an offending agent sometimes negates the presence of disease; if it does not, the disease is either assigned to the psychosomatic category or, alternatively, patients are blamed for unhealthy behaviour.

> Disease is understood as a failure in and of the individual, an isolatable "thing" that attacks the physical machine more or less arbitrarily from "outside" preventing it from fulfilling its essential "responsibilities" ... society (is considered) only as

a relatively passive medium through which "germs" pass
en route to the individual (3).

While multiple causality is sometimes acknowledged within this
framework, it largely remains in the realm of the descriptive; it
lacks an essential elaboration of the way in which multiple
causes interrelate in processes that lead to disease. For
example, malnutrition and infection might both be listed as
factors predisposing toward infant mortality, but there is no
space in the framework for an explanation of the ways in which
they interrelate with each other and with the socio-economic
environment within which disease occurs. The question of how
society is organised, the way in which it is structurally
constrained by specific dominating powers, and the relationship
between forms of social organisation and the production and
reproduction of ill health are simply never raised.

Many of the constraints that define the limits of the Palestinian
health debate today are a consequence of this mode of thinking.
It has shaped and determined the nature of much of the research
on health (4) as well as the strategies directed toward the
solution of health problems. Thus, the problems of health under
occupation are discussed in terms of the insufficient number of
hospital beds, clinics, laboratory facilities, and other
centralised and technical services. They are seen in terms of
insufficient budgets and the lack of trained specialists. They
are thought to be due to insufficient technological progress.
Progress in health is simply equated with technological progress.

The second framework for conceiving health takes the position
that ill health is a consequence of colonialism. It is largely
derived from the political/national argument and forms an
integral part of the Palestinian national consciousness. Health
and health care, as part of the national question, are today
being afforded increasing attention and prominence by the
Palestinian national movement. This is because health and its
investigation serve at least two important functions. The first
is an appeal for justice. To show that the health of the
Palestinian population living under Israeli occupation is
deteriorating is to assert further the injustice of military
rule. According to this logic, additional indictment of the
policies and practices of the military occupier, especially of
one that, like health, is based on humanitarian grounds - ought
to lead to the conclusion that health problems could only be
solved by means of a just settlement of the national question
through the erection of an independent Palestinian state (6).
Thus, health serves as a mobilising tool by appealing to humanity
for the right of Palestinians to health which in turn is linked
to national liberation.

The second function that health and its promotion serve is that
of 'steadfastness'. This term has come to embody Palestinians'
attempt to remain on their land, despite Israeli pressures to do
otherwise. By providing basic services and fulfilling what are
perceived as people's basic needs (which are not met by the

military occupier) Palestinians hope to encourage the inhabitants of the occupied territories to withstand the various pressures towards outmigration. This effort is of particular importance, since the occupied territories represent the only remaining Palestinian social entity still possessing the basis for a future reconstruction of Palestinian society. Unlike diaspora Palestinians, those who live in the occupied territories still possess land, though much of it has already been confiscated. Educational and social institutions are still functioning, though sharply constrained by military harassment. A local economy is still in evidence, despite the negative effects of colonial policies. Within the occupied territories, Palestinian life and culture have been continuous, albeit in an abnormal form, despite the loss of political identity. For the diaspora Palestinians, in contrast, life and culture have been completely and permanently disrupted. For those who are stateless refugees, the only prospects for security rest with the creation of a Palestinian state in the occupied areas. This, in turn, depends in part on the continuing physical presence of Palestinians in the West Bank and Gaza. In this context, health and health care assume an important political function.

The third framework for conceptualising health care is a more sophisticated elaboration of the mainstream national political view. It basically conceives of health as a means for achieving mass mobilisation around the issues of basic needs. Largely the initiative of the left, this approach arose as a response to the failure of the national question to adequately mobilise people, especially in rural areas, where about 70 per cent of the population live. It relies on the principle of directing the largely unmobilised population, and in particular women, into the mainstream national struggle, and uses health and other necessary services as instruments to achieve this. The credit for this trend goes to the progressive women's movement (7); for it was primarily the women's committees movement that first discovered the neglected rural areas and formulated the first concrete and workable model for this effort. Since then, a variety of committees have been created, by both men and women, to serve the needs of, and mobilise specific sectors of, the population (8). But although this third framework for conceiving health and development is by far the most interesting that has emerged; and although it is clearly influenced by a progressive ideology, it still suffers from problems it shares with the mainstream movement. In contrast with the mainstream national movement, it theoretically conceives of health as being determined not only by the national political setting (in this case colonialism) but also by other economic and social relations. In practice, however, and despite increasing popular support and substantial achievements at a certain level, it remains limited by its inability to turn theory into concrete action (9). This is the case, for example, with a popular medical movement. The movement acknowledges the mortality and morbidity differential between boys and girls (in favour of boys), but fails to take this extremely important understanding into consideration when planning and implementing health projects.

What is particularly striking about the Palestinian health debate is the tendency towards generalisation and reductionist logic. The terms of the debate are set to serve only one purpose: the incrimination of military occupation. It is as if other factors and problems affecting health, which are internal to Palestinian society, do not exist. No one doubts the substantial impact of the structures and processes of domination imposed by the military occupation on Palestinian society, and on health conditions in particular. But the health conditions are clearly affected by other factors as well, such as regional, class, and gender inequalities. The problem with the debate is its unidimensional and restricted view of health and disease, which fails to take into account the way in which Palestinian social and economic organisation interacts with other influences to produce the existing health picture. More importantly, this reductionist 'blame everything on occupation' view, locking Palestinians into the category of victims, fails to open the discussion on the possibilities of intervention in a way that goes beyond the steadfastness jargon or the services approach to health. There are always options open for action despite Israeli military rule for it is possible to mobilise people, and to help them in creating the conditions under which sanitary habits could be improved; to improve their work conditions, their incomes, and their educational levels. Intervention in these areas, and others, could yield very positive results on health, if health is conceived as a social phenomenon not solely due to the conditions of occupation. For it is here that the most dangerous aspects of the reductionist approach lie. If extended to its natural conclusion, it implies very restricted and limited possibilities for action. Short of the removal of military occupation, nothing can be done. This is the main message this approach entails. It is thus self-defeating as well, to the extent that genuine steadfastness requires that a person not have the consciousness of a victim. It is also self-defeating in that the interventions determined by it have so far yielded far from adequate results. Indeed, some claim that at times these interventions have yielded negative outcomes (10).

If the reductionist approach has gone beyond the biological paradigm for understanding health, it has only done so in order to link ill health and the national question in a manner functional to the needs of the national political argument. It has failed to locate arguments about ill health within an overall social explanation. Moreover, it essentially lumps all Palestinians together, ignoring internally generated conflicts as determinants of health. The health status of those who are poor, for instance, is not the same as of those who are rich. (Nor is the impact of military occupation equal in both cases.) Given the existing inequalities between the sexes, the health status of women is, predictably, not the same as that of men. The disparities between urban and rural areas also create differential health and disease pictures. Because the reductionist approach does not conflict with the biomedical one, nor with the power of the medical establishment, it has been effective in linking into its orbit in a workable fashion. The implications

of this are clear. Given the right political conditions, i.e.,
national liberation, the biomedical framework would be the
umbrella under which health care is conceived, planned for, and
practiced. Steadfastness funds, for example, have until recently
largely gone into the erection of more hospitals and curative
health services. Future health development plans include highly
bureaucratised medical structures and networks, and there are
numerous examples of people who advocate right-wing political
solutions with family members and/or ideological counterparts
controlling high-tech health services. Thus, the problem is a
double one. The result of this alliance has already been to
create a pervasive and dominant ideology of health under military
rule with severely limited conceptual boundaries; which sets the
stage for what may prove to be a rather unhealthy future, even
after liberation.

The consequences of the national health ideology which has been
articulated are reflected in various ways, but most strongly in
the way in which Palestinians respond to an underdeveloped
situation in health. The dominant tendency is, by and large, to
concentrate efforts on pointing out the underdevelopment of such
centralised medical facilities as hospitals, clinics, and
diagnostic centres.   The resulting tendency is to establish
curative intervention programmes that present the population with
very limited options, and fail to radically solve their health
problems.   In a nutshell, the Palestinian response to an
unhealthy situation is a palliative treatment of a recurring
disease.   It has taken the inappropriate direction of services
delivery, to a population that is mostly in need for the removal
of the cause of disease rather than the institution of centralised services (11).   In addition, the force of the interaction
between the national and biomedical arguments was for a long time
instrumental in preventing alternative views of health from
emerging.

Despite the force of this interaction, dissatisfaction with such
a problematic conceptual framework for health care has recently
been growing in the occupied territories. This appears to be at
least partially due to the evidence being drawn from field
experience.   By the beginning of the 1980s, it was becoming
increasingly clear to some that the efforts put into health
promotion during the 1970s had left the bulk of health problems
untouched (12).   The emergence of an alternative progressive
initiative embodied in the creation of the committees movement
may be an indication of this growing dissatisfaction (13).   The
women's movement is conscious of the gender question and its
relevance to health and to the general well-being of women.   Its
foundation is based in part on

     ... the importance of bridging these gaps by working at
     developing a new women's movement that advances women's
     struggle as a distinct but inseparable part of the
     struggles of the national movement (14).

The movement advances a social explanation of health and disease, and sets out to assume part of the responsibility for improving women's health.

> The combination of several factors, such as the deteriorating economic conditions, social backwardness, a lack of health and medical services under the shadow of the occupation, and the lowering of academic standards is the root of bad health conditions and has resulted in little or no health consciousness about the importance of a healthy environment and personal hygiene. This situation has put the Women's Work Committee in the forefront of many responsibilities: launching health programs, consciousness raising programs, first aid stations, guidance on personal and child care, formation of neighbourhood cleanliness committees, showing films on health, offering a number of health aid campaigns and free medical care, providing opportunities for health insurance which offers low rates for services by doctors, specialists and pharmacists (15).

The medical relief committees movement is also aware of the disparities between rich and poor, and between urban and rural areas. Its existence is seen as an attempt to fulfil the health need of those who are deprived.

> The low standard of living and the lack of appropriate medical services have contributed to the poor health conditions prevailing in the impoverished areas of the occupied territories ... Members of the Union of Palestinian Medical Relief Committees have been carrying on, voluntarily, their human duties in the impoverished Arab villages and remote communities in the West Bank since 1979 ... The Union is particularly concerned with primary health care and preventive medicine (16).

Both movements have successfully managed to cross new boundaries, by shifting the centre of the debate and action from one that concentrates on centralised urban medical facilities to one that takes into consideration a list of health priorities based on a perception of health as a social construction. The popular response to these movements has so far proven to be quite remarkable. Today, the committees are proliferating to an extent which is forcing the mainstream national and medical establishments to admit to their successes and acknowledge their presence as a social force.

What the committees movement does not appear to have succeeded in achieving so far is the formulation of programmes that concretely deal with specific inequality-related problems not directly linked with the purpose of national political mobilisation. Thus, although the women's committees are actively involved in providing such much-needed services to women as literacy education and health and child care facilities, they appear to be doing so in order to eventually expand their constituency and thus improve their bargaining power as ideological groups along national political lines.   In the end, what determines their course of action is the need of the national factions of men and women to assert their positions within the Palestinian political balance of powers.   Consequently, there have been cases of the entry of more than one women's committee into a village, and the sparking of rivalries that are not exactly in the best health interests of the people. Though the medical relief movement has successfully incorporated basic preventive principles into its framework, and has shifted the centre of attention in health care provision from the town to the rural areas, it nonetheless remains locked into the constraints of national political mobilisation and services provision.   Centralised services provision continues to be the main form of action at the village level; despite both attempts to initiate preventive measures and a gradual but slow shift of emphasis away from the doctor and the temporary cure.

Quite clearly, the importance of mass mobilisation on national political lines cannot be overemphasised.   But the problem here is one of finding a balance between national aims and the hope for a radical social transformation, and the creation of a more equitable social order.   The progressive initiative does take other aims into consideration as far as theoretical formulation is concerned; yet it does so in a manner that delineates a strategy of postponement rather than confrontation. Indeed, the primacy that is given to the national political struggle has so far been the major deterrent to the formation of a united women's movement; the splits among the women's committees follow factional lines identical to those among the national political groups.   This is still the case even now, despite the belief of all the groups involved in the need for a united women's front. It is true that the difficulty of the situation should not be underestimated; for the problematic Palestinian political scene cannot but present the progressive popular movements with serious dilemmas.   Yet the problems of class and gender should not be ignored.   One is prompted to recall the two-stage revolution theory and the way in which some elements within the radical civil rights movement in the West during the 1960s responded to feminist issues and to gender inequalities. Some Marxists viewed feminism as divisive and subordinated women's issues to the larger struggle, arguing that women would only be able to achieve their liberation after socialism was attained (17). Yet if there is a lesson to be learned from the experience of the 1960s, it is of the "need to bring together feminist consciousness with the historical and dialectical method of analysis" (18).   If conflicts other than the national one are not given more attention now, it may prove to be very difficult to give them that attention in the future.

The International Development Agency Paradigm

A fourth framework within which health care is conceived is one that can loosely be called the "international development agency" approach. Although very few Palestinians espouse this approach, it has had an impact as a result of the proliferation of aid agencies in the region. Their presence appears to be the crystallisation of the international (humanitarian as opposed to political) "response" to the plight of Palestinians and the Arab-Israeli conflict. Their approach to development is in one sense the complete opposite of the national political one. To the aid agencies, health and development are conceived in a political and economic vacuum. The notion of conflict, both internal and external to society, is also absent from this framework. The idea that health status may be determined by factors other than "backwardness" and behavioural problems is not part of this paradigm. On those occasions when the determining effects of political and economic relations on health are acknowledged, the tendency is to pay lip service to the idea, and then place it firmly on the shelf.

To the extent that this approach differs from the biomedical one, it does so by pointing to the need for decentralised services, especially in the rural areas. The emphasis, however, is generally on appropriate technology transfer and self-help projects. The implication is that the problems of underdevelopment are solely due to either the lack or the inappropriateness of technical backing; or to the personal characteristics of people: their attitudes and behaviour. Much effort is expended, for example, on teaching women how to reconstitute powdered milk under sanitary conditions, when rural households lack a clean water supply. Food aid is distributed, where it is not the absolute lack of food that is the cause of malnutrition among children. Population control is attempted where population growth is not the cause of underdevelopment problems (19). Some aid agencies have been able to break somewhat with this framework; and some of their ideas such as of self-help, community mobilisation and democratisation of decision-making, can be of value. But the way in which these notions are utilised misses the problem of the structural constraints that limit and shape the possibilities for action. The agencies also appear oblivious to the difficulties of treating villages as homogeneous entities, without regard for conflict between and within strata even at the village level. (This is a problem that they share with some Palestinian groups.)

These conceptual problems set the stage for the failure of even the best intentioned programmes. In addition, this approach sometimes places more burdens on the 'victims' than they can actually support, and with highly questionable benefits (20). The assumption that villages are homogeneous, for example, has sometimes led to the initiation of "development projects" based on recommendations by "village representatives" which turned out to place financial burdens on the poorer sectors of the village without the projects' benefits accruing to them. The problem of the agency approach to development is compounded by the Palestinians' inability to enter with its proponents into a debate that would allow for the possibility of change. Under military rule, Palestinians have neither the authority nor the control necessary to influence the policies and actions of international aid agencies. Although some Palestinians have achieved a measure of success in influencing certain policy decisions, they have done so on a purely individual, non-institutionalised basis.

Despite the partial achievements of the committees movement, reformulated understanding of health and its determinants in the context of military occupation is clearly needed. What is necessary is to enlarge the framework within which questions regarding health and disease are being raised; so as to allow for incorporating the various forces that act as determinants of the population's health status into one analytical framework.

Although the biomedical, "engineering", approach to health and health care continues to predominate in the industrialised West, mounting evidence is forcing some recognition of the social origins of health and disease. Engels, Virchow, Dubos and Selye are among those who have advocated multiple causality of disease and have acknowledged the role environment plays in determining health status. They argue that disease is in part derived from the social-material conditions under which people live (21). Within the medical tradition, the disciplines of epidemiology, preventive medicine, and community health have also recognised the environment's role in generating disease, and the importance of prevention as opposed to cures (22). Here, health is conceived as the sum of biological, environmental, and personal determinants. Water, air, housing, and work conditions form integral components of this scheme (23). These disciplines also take into account the need for activities and services other than those centred on the clinic or hospital, and the need for health care providers other than the traditional doctor and nurse (24). Health education is afforded a prominent role (25), and social and political factors are recognised as potentially instrumental in bringing about changes in the physical environment. This recognition opens up, in turn, the possibilities for reduction in morbidity and mortality rates and improvement in people's health (26).

While this extended and contextualised view of health does represent an advance over laboratory medicine, it nevertheless remains narrow and constricting. Social and political problems associated with disease are acknowledged; but the emphasis in practice remains largely on the individual and on individual behaviour, or on the description of phenomena that rule out possibilities for action other than concentration on the individual. Health workers continue to insist, for example, on teaching West Bank mothers the necessity of bathing children daily while the Israeli military refuses to connect the village with adequate supplies of potable water. Consider also, for instance, the explanation a standard text in preventive medicine offers for the causes of ill health in the Third World. Poverty, inequality, political instability, corrupt and inefficient bureaucracy, low level of literacy and poor communications, inefficient and inappropriate health services, high expenditure of wealth available for public services on arms, are all listed as causative factors (27). The limitation here is that the explanation does not allow for a deeper understanding of the causes of ill health, since no analysis is made of what lies behind these phenomena. The result of this descriptive tendency is an inability to view ill health in terms of social, economic and political relations, although it is these relations that explain the presence or absence of the listed phenomena. In this framework, no recourse is possible other than concentration on the individual, and an attempt to change behaviour. Health educators, for example, treat social class differences as influences on behaviour rather than as sources of conflict (28). Community health workers tend to restrict their activities to direct medical care and community mobilisation to solve environ-mental and attitudinal problems, without struggling also for basic social change.

This type of criticism applies equally well to the "international development agency" approach to health and development. Years of experience and the persistence of mass disease have led such agencies to reformulate their conception of health and their priorities in health care promotion (29). The Primary Health Care strategy came as a response to the inadequacy of the previous strategies. Yet despite this shift, and despite the emergence of such seemingly appropriate new concepts as community participation and mobilisation, and of emphasis on preventive medicine and the training of village health care providers, the Primary Health Care strategy is as inherently deficient as the previous Basic Needs strategy. Moreover, the deficiency is due to similar conceptual inadequacies. Not only are the new concepts largely derived from the contemporary experience of advanced industrial societies, which often has little to do with the social realities in underdeveloped countries (30), but the strategy does not work because of its failure to take into account the socio-political context within which communities operate (31). The strategy implies that individuals are free and able to choose, organise, and change their lot in life without taking into consideration the intervening effects of dominating structures. The failure of this strategy ultimately lies in the incessant refusal of those who shape it to acknowledge the necessity of critically questioning the status quo; and the way in which it determines the health status of communities, and their ability to respond to specific interventions.

The problem with this framework goes even further. The exclusion of the external structures and processes of domination and dependence determines a concentration on those aspects of the causation of ill health generated as a result of internal social problems. The operating assumption is that Third World countries have failed to achieve economic development because of endogenous defects. These are assumed to operate in isolation of the international economic order and division of labour which is, in fact, at the root of underdevelopment (32). For example, they never address such questions as the role of imperialism and colonialism in providing the foundation upon which Third World poverty is based (33); the impact of cultural imperialism on medical education and policy in those countries (34); and the role of multinational corporations in propagating and perpetuating irrational drug therapy and harmful food and drug use patterns (35). These are only some of the questions that need to be, if not elaborated, at least considered when investigating health problems in underdeveloped countries. It could be argued that such issues fall outside the disciplines of epidemiology, preventive medicine, and community health. Yet, the understanding necessary for effective action in promoting health and eradicating disease demands that these issues be incorporated into health investigations. For, as the nineteenth century physician Virchow affirmed:

> Medicine is a social science, and politics is nothing more than medicine in larger scale (36).

The Western Debate on Health

Against a background of attacks upon the powers and privileges of experts (37), social scientists have criticised the medical paradigm's conception of health as well as the modern Western medical system itself. They have seen health in terms of social, as opposed to biological, origins. They have emphasised such socio-economic determinants of health as social class, illness behaviour, cultural factors, general living conditions, and the social roles of both medicine and disease themselves (38). They have focussed special attention on Talcott Parsons' conception of the sick role as a central theoretical formulation for this framework (39), and on medicine as an instrument of social control (40). The sociology of medicine presents a challenge to the paradigm of medical knowledge to the extent that it questions the role that medicine has played in improving health (41). It views medical knowledge as a social construction and as a structure of power, where certain forms of knowledge and expertise are privileged at the expense of others (42). The various strands of the critique of medicine create a picture of the profession as an expansionist power structure with an unwarranted amount of influence on society. Medical imperialism is seen, too, as a political threat:

> It is not merely that medicine has extended its jurisdiction to cover new problems, or that doctors are professionally committed to finding disease, or even that society keeps creating disease. For if none of these were obtained today, we would still find medicine exerting an enormous influence on society. The most powerful empirical stimulus for this is the realisation of how much everyone has, or believes he has, something organically wrong with him (43).

If there is agreement over the shape of medical imperialism, it does not extend to more than the general characteristics of the beast. For the ways of its various proponents part, as a result of the divergent views on the nature of society they hold. Thus, the liberals see the problem as the power of the profession. They see medicine as a political enterprise that needs to be regulated by demanding change from the government and not the doctors (45). They neglect the relationship of the medical system to the larger social context, and thus explain the phenomenon in terms of its own internal dynamics. More radical approaches situate the power of the medical establishment within the context of a political and economic system based on private ownership and control of medical institutions (46); and link the solution to radical social change and the dismantling of capitalism. A third approach blames the medicalisation of life on medical bureaucracies organised in such a way as to produce ill health. It advocates the destruction of the medical care system and de-industrialisation of society (47). This divergence in views stems from the differences in theoretical perspectives various authors employ to examine health and medical care. The point is important; because different identifications of the cause and significance of the phenomenon of medical imperialism determine the varying courses of action proposed. As is the case with the Primary Health Care strategy in the underdeveloped world, the failure to take into account the larger socio-economic structure within which the medical empire is able to thrive obscures the ways in which effective solutions to the problem could be achieved.

Like the debate on the medical care system in industrialised countries, the debate among social scientists on health in the underdeveloped world is characterised by divergent modes of analysis and, therefore, different conclusions. Both those who have attempted intervention at least partially based on the primary health care strategy and others who have centred their attention on exposing the links between ill health and national and international political and economic relationships (48) have generated a radical critique of this perspective. All advocate changing economic and political relationships so that radical improvements in the health of Third World populations may be achieved. Navarro, for instance, argues that the problem with the analysis of medicine in Western social science is that it assumes the part (medicine) is autonomous from the whole (society). Not only does he disagree with this mode of analysis, he also believes that it serves to obfuscate rather than clarify reality. He is critical of the bias of studies that favour analysing the behaviour of individuals, to the exclusion of the behaviour of the economic and political systems which determine that behaviour. He refutes the theories that poverty is due to lack of resources, and that underdevelopment in health could be alleviated through technology transfer. To Vicente Navarro,

> The major causes of death and disease in the poor parts
> of the world today in which the majority of the human
> race lives is not a scarcity of resources, nor the

process of industrialisation, nor even the much
heralded population explosion, but rather a pattern of
control over the resources of those countries in which
the majority of the population has no control over
their resources (49).

Navarro sees the increasing economic integration of underdeveloped nations into the world-wide system of imperialism,
understood as a system of capitalist relations between developed
and underdeveloped countries, as the crucial determinant of the
present Third World health picture.

Evidence that supports this general view is plentiful, and the
framework within which the view analyses major causes of Third
World disease is more appropriate than others; but it nevertheless remains dissatisfying. The problem here is that, short of
radical political and economic transformation on a wholesale and
worldwide scale, this framework does not leave room for intervention, nor for possibilities of reform which could both improve
health conditions and mobilise people politically. Although a
Marxist one, this view appears to share these characteristics
with the mainstream Palestinian nationalist view of health
criticised earlier. The Navarro thesis suggests that capitalism
is a closed system free from contradictions. This leads to the
conclusion that improvements in health are impossible as long as
the system survives (50). Furthermore, Navarro concludes that
capitalist imperialism could not possibly result in temporary and
changeable improvements in the health of Third World people (51).
This assertion of inevitability runs dangerously close to the
unproblematised Palestinian nationalist view of the Israeli
military occupier.

Lesley Doyal's approach to the analysis of health is similar to
that of Navarro's. Her starting point is to locate health and
disease within the context of the prevailing mode of production.
Her identification of the causes of ill health in Third World
countries is basically the same as Navarro's; yet her view as to
the effects of capitalism on health is more flexible. Her
framework takes into consideration the possibility of improvements in health conditions under capitalism, although she also
argues that in the end the requirements of continued capital
accumulation come into conflict with the health needs of the mass
of the population (52). Doyal's view offers more room for the
possibility of health improvements under capitalist imperialism.
Her formulation, however, shares another inadequacy with
Navarro's. Both leave the reader unable to understand the nature
of the contradiction between ill health and internal social
organisation in underdeveloped countries. In other words, by not
focussing also on internally generated conflicts and causes of
ill health; by not taking into consideration the way in which the
powerful and dominating sectors of underdeveloped societies
interact with imperialist forces to produce and magnify health
problems, she leaves the reader with an incorrect picture of
Third World people simply as victims. It is as if internal
differentiation of society and ill health did not exist prior to

the imperialist stage of history.   It is as if the internal political economy and existing power structures have nothing to do with the production and reproduction of disease; or with the specific path of underdevelopment some Third World countries have taken.   It is as if the wretched material conditions under which most Third World people live are not also a consequence of exploitative relations generated internally.   The extremely important role that imperialism and colonialism have played in shaping the current problems of underdeveloped nations cannot be denied.   But the need to examine health and its relationship to the larger structures from the point of view of endogenous causality also cannot be ignored.

This study sets out to explore health problems from a point of view which perceives health and disease as social phenomena. With a social-medical approach in mind, it seeks to identify major health problems by focussing on those who are most biologically and socially at risk (women and children).   The biological component in the determination of the risk of disease and death is seen as important.   But it is not afforded analytical priority to the extent that the outcome of this biological risk is viewed as being ultimately determined by a constellation of economic, social and political forces.   The thesis takes into consideration the division of labour, and the way in which it affects the health of the various sectors of a population.   In terms of the impact of colonial policies on health and disease, it takes the point of view that policies do not necessarily correspond to their economic and health consequences; at times, they may generate unintended results.   It thus views conflict and its impact on health as being generated by both internal and external forces, with outcomes that can take contradictory forms. In all, it attempts to identify the major determinants of ill health by situating health and disease within their larger social, economic, and political contexts, while keeping in mind the specificity of the consequences of those determinants on health.

NOTES

1. The case of the modern X-ray machine of one of the hospitals in the area that broke down and could not be repaired for an extended period of time is an example of such a problem. Another is the case of the ambulance that was purchased by one of the hospitals and could not be used because it was discovered to be larger than the capacity of the roads in the area.

2. Look at, for instance, Winthrobe, M et al (eds), <u>Harrison's Principles of Internal Medicine</u>, 7th edition, McGraw Hill, New York, 1974; Beneson, A S (ed), <u>Control of Communicable Diseases in Man</u>, American Public Health Association, New York, 1981. For an overview of the evolution of Western scientific medicine, see Doyal, L, <u>The Political Economy of Health</u>, Pluto, London, 1983, pp. 27-36.

3. Stark, E, 'Introduction' to the special issue on health, <u>Review of Radical Political Economics</u>, Vol 9, no 1, 1977, p. v, quoted in Doyal, op cit, p. 35.

4. Baidoun, A, <u>The Role of Health in Economic Development in the West Bank</u>, Arab Thought Forum, Jerusalem, 1981; Sadler, P G & Abu-Kishk, B, <u>Palestine: Options for Development</u>, United Nations Conference on Trade and Development, Trade and Development Board, Twenty-Seventh Session, Geneva, October 1983, pp. 45-46; Katbeh, op cit.

5. See, for instance, <u>Health Conditions of the Arab Population in the Occupied Arab Territories, Including Palestine</u>, Report of the Special Committee of Experts appointed to study the health conditions of the inhabitants of the occupied territories, World Health Organisation Document A36/14, Geneva, 28 April 1983, p. 6.

6. Look at, for instance, the statement made by the Palestine Liberation Organisation representative to the Thirty-Fourth World Health Assembly in <u>Thirty-Fourth World Health Assembly, Summary Records of Committees</u>, World Health Organisation document WHA34/181/Rec/3, Geneva, 4-22 May 1981, pp. 344-346.

7. Here the term progressive is defined as a stand that advocates social advancement and the removal of gender, class and national forms of exploitation from society.

8. Examples include women's committees, medical and agricultural relief and voluntary work committees. For further information regarding the evolution of the women's committees movement in the area, see Giacaman, R, 'Palestinian Women and Development in the Occupied West Bank', Paper Presented to the 7th United Nations Seminar on the Question of Palestine, Dakkar, Senegal, August 1983.

9.   Statement of Purpose and Activities, Union of Medical Relief
      Committees, Jerusalem, 1983; Lights on Medical Problems in
      the West Bank, Union of Medical Relief Committees, Jerusal-
      em, 1984; Statement of Purpose and Activities, Voluntary
      Work Committees for the West Bank and Gaza, n.d.; Bulletin
      of Palestinian Working Women's Union in the West Bank and
      Gaza Strip, Jerusalem, August 1983; Women's Work Committees
      in the Occupied Territories, Bulletin for December 1983,
      January/February 1984.

10.   A Ramallah District village is a case in point.   To
      alleviate the health problems under occupation and solve the
      unemployment problem among physicians in the area the
      Physician's Union - supported by funds that were channelled
      across the bridge from the East Bank of the river Jordan-
      began to pay the salaries of physicians so that they would
      set up a practice in the rural areas. The physicians were
      provided rooms and some drugs, with no other support
      whatsoever.   In this village, the doctor, lacking the
      necessary support and supervision, conducted his practice by
      almost solely providing patients with drugs, without
      examining them.   According to the inhabitants of the
      community, no other attempts to alleviate the health
      problems were made. Yet other groups were not able to work
      on health projects in the village because it was already
      occupied by this physician.

11.   Giacaman, R, 'Planning for Health in Occupied Palestine',
      unpublished internal report, Birzeit University, Birzeit,
      1983.

12.   This was one of the reasons that prompted the Arab Thought
      Forum, Jerusalem, to initiate a programme for rural
      development research in the early 1980s.

13.   Look at, for instance, the statement of purpose of the Union
      of Medical Relief Committees, 1984, op cit, where the
      ultimate objectives for the activities of the Union are
      stated as "the establishment of an alternative model for a
      health programme that is compatible with the reality of the
      deteriorating health conditions", p. 1.

14.   Towards Building a United Women's Movement in the Occupied
      Territories, The Women's Work Committees in the Occupied
      Territories, Report to the Second General Conference of the
      Women's Work Committee in the Occupied Territories, March
      1983, p. 2.

15.   Ibid, p. 7.

16.   Statement of Purpose, Union of Medical Relief Committees,
      1984, p. 1, and Report of Activities during 1984, p. 1.

17.   Fee, E, 'Women and Health Care: A Comparison of Theories',
      International Journal of Health Services, Vol 5, no 3, p.
      403.

18. Ibid, p. 406.

19. Much of the exposition here came as a result of work and other type of relations between the author and some of the international development agency representatives who operate in the area, and as a result of frequent discussion among a group of Palestinians as to the role of aid agencies in the occupied territories. An example of this type of approach may be found in Health Education Project, Historical Background, Catholic Relief Services, Jerusalem, n.d., Annual Report, West Bank, Catholic Relief Services, January 1, 1982 - December, 31 1982, Jerusalem.

20. Look at, for instance, Giacaman, R, 'Community Development in the Israeli Occupied West Bank: A Case Study in Health Promotion', unpublished report, Birzeit University, Birzeit, 1983.

21. Waitzkin, H, 'The Social Origins of Illness: A Neglected History', International Journal of Health Services, Vol 11, no 1, 1981, pp. 77-103; Ehrenreich, J (ed), The Cultural Crisis of Modern Medicine, Monthly Review Press, New York, 1978, pp. 12-13.

22. See, for instance, Barker, D & Rose, G, Epidemiology in Medical Practice, 2nd edition, Churchill Livingstone, Edinburgh, 1979; Muir Gray, J & Fowler, G, Essentials in Preventive Medicine, Blackwell, Oxford, 1984; Ebrahim, G J, Child Health in a Changing Environment, Macmillan, London, 1982.

23. Ebrahim, op cit, pp. 98-100.

24. Ibid, p. 140.

25. Muir Gray & Fowler, op cit, pp. 32-44.

26. Ibid, pp. 5-8.

27. Ibid, p. 208.

28. Brown, R & Margo, G E, 'Health Education: Can the Reformers be Reformed?', International Journal of Health Services, Vol 8, no 1, 1978, p. 7.

29. Look at, for instance, the Alma-Ata Declaration, World Health Organization, 1978; Feuerstein, M T & Lovel, H, Introduction, 'Community Development and the Emergence of Primary Health Care', Community Development Journal, Vol 18, no 2, 1983, pp. 98-100.

30. Crandon, L, 'Grass Roots, Herbs, Promoters and Preventions: A Re-Evaluation of Contemporary International Health Care Planning, The Bolivian Case', Social Science and Medicine, Vol 17, no 17, 1983, pp. 1281-1289.

31. Numerous examples of this problem are found in the litera-
    ture, look at, for instance, De Kadt, E, 'Community Par-
    ticipation for Health: The Case of Latin America', World
    Development, Vol 10, no 7, 1982, pp. 573-584; Waseem, M,
    'Local Power Structures and the Relevance of Rural Develop-
    ment Strategies: A Case Study from Pakistan', Community
    Development Journal, Vol 17, no 3, 1982, pp. 225-233;
    Constantine, D C, 'Issues in Community Organisation',
    Community Development Journal, Vol 17, no 3, 1982, pp. 190-
    201; Oswald, I H, 'Are Traditional Healers the Solution to
    the Failure of Primary Health Care in Rural Nepal?', Social
    Science and Medicine, Vol 17, no 5, 1983, pp. 255-257;
    Giacaman, R, 'The Raymah Health Project: An Evaluation';
    unpublished report, Oxfam, Oxford, 1984.

32. For an elaboration of the inadequacy of the endogenous
    argument see, for instance, Roxborough, I, Theories of
    Underdevelopment, Macmillan, London, 1979; Alavi, H &
    Shanin, T, Introduction to the Sociology of 'Developing
    Societies', Macmillan, London, 1982; Amin, S, Imperialism
    and Unequal Development, The Harvester Press, Sussex, 1977.

33. Doyal, op cit, pp. 96-137; Feder, E, 'Plundering the Poor:
    The Role of the World Bank in the Third World', Internation-
    al Journal of Health Services, Vol 13, no 4, 1983, pp. 649-
    660; De Castro, J, The Geopolitics of Hunger, Monthly Review
    Press, New York, 1977.

34. Donaldson, P J, 'Foreign Intervention in Medical Education:
    A Case Study of the Rockefeller Foundation's Involvement in
    a Thai Medical School', in Navarro, V (ed), Imperialism,
    Health and Medicine, Pluto, London, 1982, p.126; Lall, D &
    Bibile, S, 'The Political Economy of Controlling Transna-
    tionals: The Pharmaceutical Industry in Sri Lanka, 1972-
    1976', in Navarro (ed), op cit, pp. 253-282. See also the
    more popular literature on the subject, such as Bull, D, A
    Growing Problem: Pesticides and the Third World Poor, Oxfam,
    Oxford, 1982; Melrose, D, Bitter Pills: Medicines and the
    Third World Poor, Oxfam, Oxford, 1982.

36. Virchow, R, Disease, Life and Man, translated by L J Rather,
    Stanford University Press, Stanford, 1958, p. 106, quoted in
    Waitzkin, op cit, p. 89.

37. Strong, P M, 'Sociological Imperialism and the Profession of
    Medicine: A Critical Examination of the Thesis of Medical
    Imperialism', Social Science and Medicine, Vol 13A, 1979, p.
    199.

38. See, for instance, Susser, M W & Watson, W, Sociology in
    Medicine, Oxford University Press, London, 1971; Robinson,
    D, Patients, Practitioners and Medical Care: Aspects of
    Medical Sociology, Heinemann, London, 1983.

39. Ehrenreich, B & Ehrenreich, J, 'Medicine and Social
     Control', in Ehrenreich, op cit, p. 43.

40. Ibid, pp. 39-79 and 80-100. See also Kennedy, I, The
     Unmasking of Medicine, George Allen & Unwin, Boston, 1981;
     Friedson, E, Professions of Medicine, Dodd Mead, New York,
     1970.

41. Mckeown, T, The Modern Rise of Population, Arnold, London,
     1976; Mckeown, T, The Role of Medicine: Dream Mirage or
     Nemesis, Blackwell, Oxford, 1979; Somers, A & Somers, H,
     Health and Health Care in Perspective, Aspen Systems
     Corporation, Maryland, 1977.

42. Wright, P & Treacher, A (eds), The Problem of Medical
     Knowledge: Examining the Social Construction of Medicine,
     Edinburgh University Press, Edinburgh, 1982.

43. Zola, I K, 'Medicine as an Institution of Social Control',
     in Ehrenreich, op cit, p. 91.

44. Strong, op cit, p. 200.

45. Kennedy, op cit.

46. Doyal, op cit, pp. 37-44.

47. Illich, I, Medical Nemesis: The Expropriation of Health,
     Pantheon, New York, 1976.

48. De Kadt, op cit; Turshen, M & Thebaud, A, 'International
     Medical Aid', Monthly Review, Vol 33, 1981, pp. 39-50;
     Makhoul, N 'Assessment and Implementation of Health Care
     Priorities: Incompatible Paradigms and Competing Social
     Systems', Social Science and Medicine, Vol 19, no 4, 1984,
     pp. 373-384; Navarro, V, Medicine Under Capitalism, Croom
     Helm, London, 1976, and Imperialism, Health and Medicine,
     Pluto, London, 1982; Doyal, op cit.

49. Navarro, V, Imperialism, op cit, p. 7.

50. Reidy, A, 'Marxist Functionalism in Medicine: A Critique of
     the Work of Vicente Navarro on Health and Medicine', Social
     Science and Medicine, Vol 19, no 9, 1984, pp. 897-910.

51. For a very interesting elaboration of the notion of
     imperialism as a progressive force see Warren, B, Im-
     perialism Pioneer of Capitalism, Verso, London, 1980.
     Though Warren's conclusions are rejected by this author, on
     both theoretical and practical grounds, his thesis does
     represent a genuinely thought-provoking reading.

52. Doyal, op cit, pp. 22-23.

CHAPTER TWO

APPROACH, TOOLS AND METHODS

The decision to investigate health status at the village level
was not accidental. It represented an attempt to create a more
informed health policy as a basis for action. In 1980, Birzeit
Women's Charitable Society in conjunction with Birzeit University
were in the process of drawing up the initial plans for a village
health programme. The programme was loosely formulated around
the Primary Health Care model, which provides essential health
services at the local level, including health education and
preventive services. It also provides for mobilisation. At the
time, the need for health services in the nearby villages was
evident. None of the twenty or so villages that surround Birzeit
had any form of modern health care. The indigenous medical
system, in addition, was in the process of being dismantled,
leaving the inhabitants with very limited options for health
care. The mood predominating in the area was one where local
Palestinian institutions were beginning to perceive their role in
a new light. Since basic needs were not being met by the Israeli
military, Palestinian institutions and organisations began to
accept the responsibility of at least partially fulfilling them.
In the absence of a national government interested in the welfare
of the people, these institutions defined their role as support-
ing a deteriorating services infrastructure and creating new
ones.

With intervention projects and the state of the health debate in
mind, the research scheme was conceived as an attempt to
delineate the health picture of a particular group in a region
where the health map was largely blank. The intention was not to
generalise from the experience; but rather to raise questions and
delineate patterns that could not be elaborated in a macro-level
study. It was thought, in addition, that this research would
prove useful in consolidating relations between the village
communities and both institutions. Consolidation was necessary
on two grounds: first, so that institution members could gain a
further understanding of village life; and second, so that a
relationship of trust and open discussion could be established
which could form the basis for later community mobilisation.

The investigation began with several fundamental questions: what
are the basic health problems at the village level, and why do
they occur? Are there differences in health status among members

of village communities, and, if so, what are the reasons for
those variations? Are multiple causes involved, including socio-
economic conditions? How do the communities deal with health and
disease, and how could health problems be solved?

The Design

Three nearby village communities were chosen for investigation.
The choice of villages posed a problem, due to the limited
possibilities available. We had the option of choosing villages
with varying characteristics, where these differences were
significant to health. But this choice would have posed several
problems. A major one was distance and access to transport
facilities. We were faced with probable frequent interruptions,
due to the presence of military checkpoints, university closures
by order of the military government, and at times curfews. This
meant that the closer our communities were to us, the more chance
we had of completing our investigation without serious disrup-
tions. Because of these factors, and such others as the
difficulties of managing a large research team under these
conditions, we decided that it was most realistic, although not
necessarily ideal, to choose communities close to Birzeit
University, and thus easily reached. The final choice of the
three communities was based on three other considerations. The
first was the need to examine a total population of at least 2000
people, with the number of married women of childbearing age as
close to 300 as possible. This was essential in order to yield
meaningful demographic and other statistical parameters. The
second was the desire to work with communities where relations of
trust were already established or could easily be achieved. The
third was our interest in examining the difference in health
status between communities that had a potable water supply and
those that did not. In our area, only one village was connected
to a piped water supply. It was thus chosen as a basis upon
which comparisons could be made. Eventually we chose three
villages, none of which was further than ten kilometres from the
university, and with a combined population of 2188. Even then,
the original research design had to be modified on more than one
occasion, due to constraints imposed by the problems of military
occupation.

The design of the survey centres around elaborating the elements
of a health profile for women of childbearing age and for
children under the age of three years. It is generally accepted
that children's health is the barometer which reflects the
overall health of a population. Due to biological and social
factors, children also tend to be more at risk of becoming sick
and dying than the rest of the population. Women of childbearing
age likewise constitute a high-risk group. We hoped that
examining the two groups would yield results that would indicate
the basis upon which village health programmes could be designed
and implemented. In addition to this concentration on women and
children, we surveyed the total population of the three villages
as a way of answering some of our questions. We preferred this

to the sample method for two reasons. First, by widening our perspective to include some information pertaining to the entire population, we gained the advantage of being able to confidently generalise our results for the entire village. Second, in order to develop a stratified sample adequate for the purpose of generalisation we had to have a level of understanding both of the village communities and of the health picture there, which could only have been obtained through a time-consuming process precluded by circumstances.

The Initial Survey (May-August, 1981)

We surveyed all households in the three villages. A household was defined as the physical and social unit joined by one household head and utilising a common cooking and eating area (sometimes this is a kitchen; at other times it is simply an area inside or close to the dwelling). After pilot testing, four types of questionnaires were constructed. The number of test cases was 36, out of a total of 336 households (i.e., 10 per cent of the total). Information regarding such general population characteristics as age and sex distribution, literacy, education-al levels, and occupation was obtained for each household. Information on household characteristics thought to be important for health, such as size of dwelling, presence or absence of amenities, and land and animal ownership was also obtained. Birth histories and behavioural and attitudinal parameters formed the core of the questionnaire administered to women of childbear-ing age. Birth, feeding, health, and disease histories were obtained for children under three years of age. Data on illnesses by type occurring during the two weeks immediately preceding the survey was also obtained for the entire family (Appendix 2).

Households were classified by wealth status into three categor-ies (high, medium and low), based on information supplied by four local informants for each village. The average of the four scores obtained for each household was used as the wealth index for that household. This classification of wealth status was based principally on the perceived purchasing power of individual households. It included land ownership, incomes from paid work, and remittances from migrant workers abroad. Information regarding migrant workers was obtained for the sons of the household head only, on the assumption that it was probably only sons who contributed remittances to the family at home. This procedure also avoided counting individuals more than once, if identification through other kinship relations were used. The scores obtained from the four informants were generally very similar. Moreover, cross-tabulation of household wealth status with such indicators of financial status as the presence or absence of selected amenities in the dwelling, the number of migrant workers abroad, and the number of male household members currently working all yielded strong and positive associations. Finally, classification lists were reviewed by village Mukhtars and then adopted for purposes of analysis. On the whole, although this method of income status assessment may not be ideal, it was deemed sufficiently reliable for our purposes.

The respondents in all cases were women. For the general household and family members data, the wife of the head of household was the usual respondent. All interviews, however, were conducted in the presence of most or all of the household women, usually with neighbours and friends present. This method of collective interviewing offered both an advantage and a disadvantage. On the one hand, the presence of other women did help respondents to more accurately answer the questions, and perhaps better remember incidents that had occurred a long time before, such as births and deaths of children. On the other hand, this lack of privacy made respondents slightly reluctant to express their opinions. Such was the case, for example, when information regarding the use of contraception was being sought. But there was no choice in the matter; the conditions and ways of life in the village precluded the possibility of private encounters.

We restricted physical measurements and laboratory examinations to children under the age of three years and married women of childbearing age. The procedures and techniques described by Jelliffe (1) were used to measure the weights and lengths of children. Children's ages were obtained from either birth certificates or immunisation cards. Both sources were believed to be accurate. Stool samples of children were collected using special stool collection containers never used before; these were opened for the first time to be partially filled with the stool preservative polyvynil alcohol. All stool specimens were concentrated using the formalin-ether concentration technique. Iodine and trichrome staining procedures were used to aid the identification of intestinal parasites, especially protozoa (2). Blood of mothers was obtained from the third fingertip, via capillary tubes, and haematocrit levels were obtained using the method recommended by the World Health Organisation (3).

The Follow-ups

The follow-ups had two purposes: to find out if there were seasonal variations in morbidity; and to discern possible changes in the way the communities' inhabitants responded to disease. This was thought to be important; by the end of 1981, Birzeit Women's Charitable Society had launched its village health work programme. It had succeeded in expanding its health services to include a daily curative clinic, centralised prenatal care for women, and well and sick baby clinics, all based on a regular schedule for these three villages among twenty-three others. These services were heavily subsidised and thus affordable by most. The follow-ups were restricted to households that had married women of childbearing age, mostly because of financial and logistical constraints. There were 244 of those, or 73 per cent of the total number of households. The follow-ups were executed in October 1981, January, April, and July 1982. The same questionnaire was administered, in the semi-structured form used in the survey, for all the follow-ups. The wives of the heads of the household were asked questions regarding incidence of disease among family members within the two-week period immediately preceding the follow-up. They were then asked what treatment had been followed (Appendix 2).

The Survey: Practice

To suggest that the various components of the research project were crystal clear and coherent from the outset would be misleading. In 1981, both the Charitable Society women and I were far from clear as to the best ways to initiate the necessary contacts with the various villages and to prepare the ground for the planned village health worker programme. The problem for me was also the choice of communities for research purposes. What we were looking for was a balance between local need and adequate potential for project success. At the time we did not want to risk implementing the project in a locality where there was only a small chance of success; for the idea was to utilise the first project as an example through which other communities could be mobilised. Thus, the choice of community for research purposes was also determined by this practical consideration. To begin the search for the appropriate communities, we defined our catchment area as those villages that were either connected to Birzeit town, where our base was, by roads and public transportation, or those that were within ten kilometres of the Charitable Society clinic. We began the search by simply visiting the closest villages first.

Our first attempt was catastrophic. We landed in a village, the closest to Birzeit. It was one where, because of the history of relations between the two towns, the inhabitants could not help but think of Birzeit and its Charitable Society in competitive terms. Although we were received politely, the response was a firm No thank you, we do not need your health project. The experience forced us to reconsider our strategy, and to begin thinking about alternative methods of entry into villages. We began to learn how to prepare the way for our meeting with village notables by involving university students from these villages in the initial contact. We began to choose localities for visits based on whether the inhabitants were receiving care at the Society clinic or not; and therefore based on these communities' knowledge of the Society women and their efforts in health care. The new strategy proved to be a lot more fruitful. After that unfortunate first attempt, we were generally met with a considerable amount of enthusiasm. Our village visits continued for about four months. Much of our initial groundwork was intended to gain legitimacy and establish a relation of trust.

Most of our meetings were with men: the Mukhtars, other village notables, and village teachers. In order to gain access to the world of women, we had first to earn the approval of the men. As women, we did not encounter problems in meeting men. For we were recognised as different, townspeople, and subject to a different moral code. The fact that we were attached to Birzeit University did help legitimise our role. In the end, the fact that we were women and from the university offered us an advantage generally not afforded to men; we were actually able to move between the worlds of men and women rather easily. We began to realize how different these two worlds were, and the impact this difference had on the perceptions of village men and women. In addition, as women we were perceived as less of a threat than men; therefore the tendency was to provide us with information we needed without excessive caution.

All of us were health care professionals, having been trained within the biomedical framework. Being town dwellers was another potential handicap, because village life was generally remote from our experience. Although the Society women were knowledge-able concerning problems of village health, this knowledge was limited by its one-sidedness. It was primarily built on centralised clinical experience, where the interactions were more or less restricted to the Society women's providing health care and the village inhabitants receiving it. Our lack of under-standing of village life, its structures and processes, meant trouble on more than one occasion. We once unwittingly sided with one village faction against another. The result was the ignition of an age-old feud between the two factions, which prompted one of the more reasonable village leaders to quickly request our departure. The remarkable event was that a few months later the village representative came to us in Birzeit to request our return, and the reinstatement of the village health project. They must have strongly felt the need of health care and our services to be willing to reestablish relations with us.

Thus we sometimes learned the hard way about village social structure, and the fact that village stratification did exist along both vertical (clan or extended family) and horizontal (class) lines. This discovery was actually quite surprising; much of the community mobilisation literature we were reading at the time portrayed villages as homogeneous units and led to the impression that conflict in the village was nonexistent. Where it was recognised, it was seen as of minor importance. It was not seen as posing a problem to think about and look for when attempting to mobilise communities around development projects.

As we worked, we began to realize how little we really knew, not only about village life but also about health and disease as social phenomena. But we did not accept this realization readily. On many occasions we resisted criticism by social scientist colleagues; we claimed that what they were talking about was social science and not health, and that social science was not our concern. We eventually conceded its importance, however, in view of the hard-hitting evidence being generated by our field visits, mistakes, and follies. In the end, two social scientists were appointed as consultants for the research portion of the project. Here a new problem arose. The social scientists wanted to broaden the questionnaire to include data on migrants, land, tenure, farm budgets, and many other subjects apparently outside the scope of our project. The potential questionnaires grew thicker, and anxiety levels over administering them rose higher. The issues were settled by a compromise. But some of the questions included at the insistence of the social scientists proved to be crucial elements for data analysis. I must also admit that it was through insights gained from discussions with them that much confusing material was eventually clarified.

We finally chose the first three villages to initiate the village health worker programme and the research project, based on a balance between need and community enthusiasm for the potential projects. We decided that only two persons would conduct interviews and administer questionnaires, the author and one other well experienced person. We divided each village into quarters and set out to cover one side of the dirt road each, beginning with the areas closest to the village entrance. Each day, including holidays, we went to the village early in the morning, and stayed there usually until around sunset. Each evening, we would meet to discuss the day's work and prepare for the next day. We made appropriate corrections, added notes, and exchanged insights. What really surprised us was the extent of curiosity our presence generated in the village. The women were especially curious, and did not seem to have trouble expressing their feelings. On numerous occasions it was we who were subjected to interviews.

To conduct interviews we needed determination. The women interviewed had their own agendas, and we were incessantly grilled with such questions as 'How many children do you have?', 'Why aren't you married?', 'Where are your parents?' and 'Do they have money?' As we were being interviewed we would try to slip in a question or two in the midst of the confusion. The experience slowly led us away from the stereotyped images we had of "poor, weak and obedient" peasant women; these women embodied Palestinian strength and determination. We had begun by looking at the women condescendingly: We were there to help them, to "raise their consciousness". But these women did not necessarily need their consciousness raised. They knew what was going on and they understood how to solve their problems. What they needed was the power and authority to change their lives.

To the women, although Palestinian, we represented a phenomenon from outer space: our clothes; the way we talked; the way we handled ourselves; and our ability to handle men so apparently easily were but some symbols of the differences and the divide that separates rural from urban. Religion, marriage, husbands, children, and university life were the topics of most interest. Politics, on the other hand, was often avoided; it was neither a woman's domain, nor a topic that could be discussed without worrying about deleterious consequences. The fear of military retaliation always filled the air. The nature of the interviews, then, was not really left entirely to us, or to study design. The situation dictated semi-structured, somewhat open-ended

sessions.   Enforcing the structure we had originally planned
would have been rather intrusive given the needs and interests of
the respondents.   In retrospect, it would probably also have
meant the loss of the many insights and the increased understanding of village life that were by-products of casual discussion
and observation.

Our arrival at the village was generally signalled by the
children. Without knowing exactly how, we would find ourselves
encircled.   We then would be directed to our destination, where
neighbours and friends would sometimes have already gathered to
meet us.   Coffee or tea would be served; a variety of topics
covered; and then the interview would proceed.   Interview
questions had to be inserted in between other conversation that
was taking place, cries of children and a variety of other
interruptions.   Attempting to keep a strict timetable was not
only futile, but would have created much frustration. But by far
the most disruptive effects came from the presence of the men of
the house.   On those occasions when they were there, they tended
to leave no room for the participation of women in the discussion; nor for their response to questions.   They were obviously
in charge; and therefore felt the need to receive all of our
attention, including on those occasions when we wanted to know
the views of women.   The reaction of women, moreover, was
generally either one of silence or of taking a secondary role in
the presence of their husbands, male adult children, or the head
of the household. Our insistence, however, did yield results.

Power and authority in the village really are in the hands of men
and even of male children. While, for example, a 12- or 13-year-
old boy might not yet have power (he is not yet earning money),
he already has authority over his sisters, his mother and even
his grandmother.   Even at the household level we had to pass
through the men to reach the women. At times, boys in transition
to manhood would come to the doorstep of a house and block our
entrance until we had satisfied their need for an explanation of
our presence.   They would want us to interview them instead of
their mothers because they were the "men" of the household.   The
authority given to them is based on the expectation that as
bread-winners they will provide for the family, combined with and
reinforced by the legal system.

Entering the villages under the banner of a prospective health
project was a mixed blessing for research purposes.   The
possibility of rewards for answering questions meant that people
had a lot of enthusiasm and willingness to provide us with the
necessary time and the responses to questions.   But, with the
idea of the health project looming on the horizon, responses to
certain questions were far from satisfactory. To the villagers,
a health project was conceived of as a charitable endeavour; the
poorer you were, the more likely it was that you would receive
some support or subsidy from the Society. This, coupled with the
general reluctance of people to reveal information regarding
income and land ownership to outsiders meant almost totally
meaningless income and land ownership data.   The reluctance to

give information itself is completely intelligible in the context of military occupation, widespread land confiscation and a long history of occupation, oppression and exploitation through an unjust taxation system. Luckily, we established a good working relationship with selected village members from the beginning. Our informants alerted us to the problem at a very early stage. We thus abandoned the attempt to generate reliable financial status data through information obtained from individuals and began the search for alternative methods. As described earlier, the informants solved the problem by classifying households into one of three wealth categories.

There were other difficulties that sometimes made field work imperfect and unbearable. For logistical reasons, we were unable to complete the anthropometric exams on children at the same time we conducted the interviews. These exams were done about one month later. Thus, although, for instance, we were aware of the need to relate diarrhoea to nutritional status, the opportunity was lost. There was a cholera scare in the Ramallah area around the time we were collecting children's stool samples (we continued collecting). Less than ideal village conditions made it almost impossible to ensure adequate collection without the undue worry of possible contamination. Ultimately, our handling of the stools and the cholera scare both ended uneventfully, but these were not exactly pleasant times. We worked right through Ramadan (the Muslim fasting month), which meant no food or drink for the entire day. The month turned out to be one of the hottest, and therefore a most difficult and unfortunate time for field work and for pleasant tempers. In the end, we thought it a feat that the initial survey, which began in May, ended by the beginning of September and without extended deviations from the planned timetable.

Though comprehensive analysis of the data did not take place until 1985, we did an initial and quick tabulation of the results of physical measurements and an initial review of the question-naires in September 1981. Some of the results were incorporated into the village health work/health education training courses the Society was offering to village women. Starting in October 1981, the follow-ups began, and so did a working relationship with a few community members that continues until today. During that year, we did several things simultaneously. Newly trained village women administered the follow-ups. Piecemeal data analysis alerted us to inconsistencies and odd results, and made us return to the villages for further extended discussion with trusted community members. We also discovered on more than one occasion that knowledge and behaviour did not always correspond; and we began to understand the limitations of survey methods. Village health centres were also being set up during that year. We were actively participating in designing and executing these programmes alongside community members who took initiative. In summary, the year proved to be the foundation upon which most of the data analysis and interpretation was based. For it was then that we consolidated our understanding of village life; ap-preciated what observation and participation had to offer a

researcher, even in health care; and began to really grasp the
meaning of structural and material constraints to village
mobilisation and action. We also began to wonder about the
limitations of our health education efforts, given the material
and environmental impediments to the utilisation of knowledge.
We began to question the usefulness of the international
development agency approach, which generally portrayed village
communities as independent entities completely divorced from a
setting that determined the feasibility and limitations of
village action. In other words, unlike some who are critical of
the mainstream approach to development, we began with action and
came to an alternative theory as a result of our experiences.
This experience, including our failures, did more to transform us
than to change the villages.

This is not to say that the village health project was not
partially successful. The health education classes picked up a
substantial amount of popularity, partly because of a specific
event. In one village, a woman attending her precious goat's
delivery managed to save the life of the newly born and asphyxi-
ated kid by applying mouth-to-mouth resuscitation techniques she
had been taught in health education classes. The anecdote spread
like wildfire. Eventually, we ceased to be the initiators in
village mobilisation through our visits. Instead, village
leaders began to visit the Society clinic and request its health
education services, based on what they had heard about the
project in other villages. Yet mobilisation remained largely at
the level of behavioural modification. It centred around
individual and collective self-help within the framework of the
village. Though helpful, these activities remained limited. If
there is a lesson to be learned from the experience, it is that
what village communities mostly need are the organisational and
political skills to challenge their political, economic, and
social relationships with the larger context, relationships that
are the cause of disease to begin with. That instead became the
task of the progressive committees movement.

The Analysis

Although piecemeal data analysis began in 1981 and continued in a
sporadic fashion until the end of 1983, the disrupted nature of
the process necessitated a repetition in 1985 of most of the
steps previously taken.

Nutritional status assessment was expressed by Mclaren and Read's
weight/length/age classification, derived from the Harvard standards. As a percentage of ideal weight/length/age, the observed
weights that were more than 110 per cent of this ideal were classified as overweight; between 90-110 per cent as normal; between
85-90 per cent as mild malnutrition; between 75-85 per cent as
moderate malnutrition; and those less than 75 per cent of the
ideal as severe malnutrition. Length deficit was not part of the
classification, except with children who were over 90 per cent of
their expected length/age. Such children were classified as nu-

tritional dwarfs, to indicate episodes of past malnutrition (4).
The Mclaren and Read method was chosen over other methods,
especially classifications that are based on weights alone,
because of the latters' many, now recognised inadequacy. As
Mclaren and Read point out, the drawbacks include the lack of a
local standard for comparison; and the inappropriate nature of an
international, or Western, standard in most developing countries.
Moreover, those classifications assume that children of a certain
age should ideally have the same weight, regardless of their size
as measured by length. This method, as the authors point out, is
incapable of distinguishing between past and present effects of
malnutrition. As a result, those children who were malnourished
in the past would appear to have a deficit in weight for age,
even though their weight in proportion to their length, which is
stunted, may be normal. Simplicity was also a factor in our
choice; the Mclaren and Read classification can be easily applied
(Appendix 3).

Estimation of fertility was based on number of children ever born
classified by duration of marriage. We obtained this information
from all currently married women up to the age of 49 years. We
then estimated levels of natural fertility from reported parity
by duration of marriage, based on the procedures described in the
United Nations Manual X on indirect techniques for demographic
estimation (5). Several considerations determined the use of
this particular method. First, we believed that duration-of-
marriage-based estimates would yield more accurate results,
because the accuracy of marriage duration reports could be cross-
and double-checked more easily than age reports. This was
especially true of women over 30 years old. Second, the
assumptions underlying this method: very limited practice of
voluntary birth control; and infrequent childbearing by women
outside marriage, seemed to hold true in the population we
studied. Third, only seven out of a total of 272 married women
of childbearing age were in their second union. The average
parities for currently married women by time elapsed since first
union, regardless of the number of unions provided a reasonable
basis for fertility estimation, since the introduction of error
or bias due to the number of unions was minimal. Fourth, in the
absence of a proper and reliable reporting system for births and
deaths at the village level, this method seemed to yield
fertility estimates as reliable as could possibly be obtained,
under the conditions of the study's execution. Last, the method
is relatively easy to apply. We derived an estimate of the birth
rate from the fertility estimates and followed the method's steps
from there.

Child mortality calculations were based on the number of children
ever born and dead of ever married women between the ages of 15
and 49, classified by duration of marriage. We first classified
children born and dead by sex, and then computed estimates of
childhood mortality by sex and for both sexes together (6). The
problem with this method is the assumption that the child's risk
of dying is a function only of the child's age and not of such
other factors as the child's birth order or the mother's age (7).

However, because children of younger mothers generally experience above average mortality risks, the method disregards the reports of women aged 15 to 19 years. Another important problem with this method is that it assumes fertility and childhood mortality have remained constant in the recent past. In the case of this survey's data, however, although fertility was thought to have remained constant in the recent past, child mortality was not. To solve the problem of changing mortality rates, the method allows for the calculation of time-location estimates, that is, some particular period t(x), during which a corresponding value of childhood mortality was prevalent. Time-location estimates, however, depend on the assumption that the rate of change of infant mortality is roughly constant. Given that there appeared to be no reason to think otherwise, this assumption was held as valid. Duration of marriage rather than age was chosen as the basis of calculations for the same reasons that were discussed under fertility calculations.

Computer coding was performed in two stages. Part of the database was already precoded in the questionnaire. The rest was recoded and kept on computer tape along with the questionnaire material. After data clean-up and utilising the SPSS computer programme (8), simple frequencies by village were obtained. We soon discovered that the three villages shared very similar general characteristics, and that the results of physical and other measurements were very similar for all. We therefore decided to perform the analysis on the three villages as one entity, not only when dealing with fertility and mortality data but also when examining health and other parameters. This step was additionally justified because the three villages were within a three-to-four kilometre distance of each other, and shared similar geographic and ecological characteristics. Had these villages been in North Yemen, for instance, they would have most certainly been considered different quarters of one village.

We then cross-tabulated the health parameters with a variety of possible determinants. These included biological (age); socio-behavioural/environmental (child's gender, child-feeding and weaning patterns, presence or absence of selected household amenities, and mothers' educational levels); and financial status (number of household migrants, male workers living at home, and type of employment) determinants. This process continued until patterns were discerned. From then on, a process of stepwise elimination yielded a workable quantity of parameters, which were subjected to cross-tabulation as well as Chi-square significance testing (9). What was particularly interesting here was that (unlike what might have been expected) there was no relationship between the type of employment of the male household members and such other socio-economic status indicators as the educational level and health status indicators of family members. On the other hand, strong and positive association was found between the informant's wealth status categorisation and the number of locally employed and migrant workers in a household; the availability of selected household amenities; the educational levels of household members and the health status indicators of

mothers and children.   In these villages, the household's socio-
economic status is apparently less a reflection of the type of
employment its members hold than of the cumulative effects of
employment locally and abroad.   This evidence further supports
our decision to select the informants' wealth status categorisation (as opposed to each financial status parameter above) as a
health status determinant, and as the basis upon which to conduct
the analysis.   Significance testing was applied only in cases
when there was a need to generalise for the entire population the
findings for one of its sectors, say, in this case, for children
under 3 years old.   Even then, those generalisations were
interpreted with caution, and only against the background of
observation material and an understanding of village life and its
processes.   For although significance testing can be of use in
general, it is limited to the description of aggregates rather
than the explanation of phenomena.   Its use at most times amounts
to no more than bad statistical inference (10).

NOTES

1. Jelliffe, D B, <u>The Assessment of the Nutritional Status of
    the Community</u>, World Health Organisation, Geneva, 1966.

2. <u>Manual of Basic Techniques for a Health Laboratory</u>, World
    Health Organisation, Geneva, 1980, pp. 165-167, 173-174;
    Levinson, S & McFate, R, <u>Clinical Laboratory Diagnosis</u>, Lea
    and Febiger, Philadelphia, 1969, p. 261.

3. <u>Manual of Basic Techniques</u>, op cit, pp. 379-383.

4. See Mclaren, D S & Read, W, 'Weight/Length Classification of
    Nutritional Status', <u>The Lancet</u>, 2.8.1975, pp. 219-221.
    Expected lengths for age were drawn from Simmonds, S,
    Vaughan, P & Gunn, S W, <u>Refugee Community Health Care</u>,
    Oxford University Press, Oxford, 1983, Appendix 2, Tables 3
    and 4, pp. 310-311.

5. <u>Manual X: Indirect Techniques for Demographic Estimation</u>,
    United Nations, New York, 1983, pp. 64-69 and Annex 1, pp.
    225-227.

6. Computation procedures followed the steps that were
    delineated in <u>Manual X</u>, op cit, pp. 81-85. This method of
    calculation was originally obtained from Frederic Shorter,
    The Population Council, Cairo, Egypt.

7. <u>Manual X</u>, op cit, p. 73.

8. Nie, N H et al, <u>Statistical Package for the Social Sciences</u>,
    2nd edition, McGraw Hill, New York, 1975.

9. Look at, for instance, Blalock, H M, <u>Social Statistics</u>, 2nd
    edition, McGraw Hill, Tokyo, 1972, pp. 275-287.

10. For an interesting elaboration of the problem look at
    Morrison, D E & Henkel, R E, <u>The Significance Test Con-
    troversy</u>, Butterworths, London, 1970. One ought to add that
    if it is believed that in behavioural sciences significance
    testing has been badly used, one cannot imagine what could
    be said regarding its use in the medical sciences!

CHAPTER THREE

THE COMMUNITIES

The three rural communities share many of their characteristics
with most other West Bank highland villages. Located within a
15-kilometre radius of the nearest town centre, Ramallah, access
to the town and all that it can offer is not a severe problem. A
twice-daily bus normally operates. It transports the bulk of
those who daily leave the village to seek employment, either in
the West Bank or in Israel as wage labourers. The majority of
these are, of course, men. Other than the bus, a string of
privately owned taxis, called "services", operate on a cost-
sharing basis, and help keep the village-town connection alive
during the day. Since these are irregular and infrequent, some
villagers simply opt to walk a distance of three-to-seven
kilometres to the Birzeit village T-junction (where Birzeit
University is located) rather than wait. Once the Birzeit
junction is reached, it is easy to reach Ramallah, for the
Ramallah-Birzeit line is regular, frequent, and subsidised by the
university to solve its own transportation problems.

Ramallah occupies a central position in village life. As the
administrative centre for the district, it serves most of the
villagers' needs. It is there that the villagers pursue official
and legal matters. It is there that they sell their produce, and
buy whatever the Ramallah market has to offer. It is there that
they seek health care, and where students seek secondary and
post-secondary education. And, in the past, it was there that
the villagers sought work. This is different today, for many
instead work in Israel, as construction workers.

This dependence on the town is typical of most other villages in
the area. A basically stagnant village economy, coupled with
obviously inadequate infrastructural networks for basic services,
makes the town-village bond inseparable. In 1981, there were no
modern health facilities of any sort in the three villages.
Around-the-clock electrical supply was still a relatively recent
phenomenon. Only one of the villages was connected to a
telephone and a municipal piped water supply. The other two are
still in the process of struggling with the military government
for permission to connect themselves with Birzeit's piped water
supply (1). In 1981, as today, there were no secondary schools
in the villages. A few village stores were in operation. They
mostly supplied canned foods; powdered milk and other infant

weaning foods; Israeli-made white bread and biscuits; and such scattered other items as batteries, shaving paraphernalia, cigarettes and soft drinks - items which require experience in "modern" life and which give no indication where in the developed or underdeveloped world the village is located. Perhaps the village stores best capture the image of the remarkable changes in village life and consumption patterns during the past twenty years or so. One would expect that had the stores existed twenty or more years ago they would have stocked lentils, spices, locally made soap, sugar, and other items that would have revealed consumption patterns compatible with traditional village life.

The absence of public or community centres, except perhaps the mosques, and on special occasions the <u>Mukhtar's</u> house, was noticeable. The <u>Diwan</u> (2) tradition of hospitality disappeared in the 1950s, according to the villagers, without being replaced with an equivalent alternative. Youth clubs are a very recent and growing phenomenon; but they serve different functions than the <u>Diwan</u> - mostly political mobilisation - and only cater to the needs of the younger males. These villages represent more a creche for the very young and haven for the retired older generation than a bustling and productive community. The absence of community or meeting centres for women was even more noticeable. Other than the village spring and the <u>Taboun</u> (traditional oven usually shared by several families), women could only meet other women in homes or within the immediate vicinity of their homes. This was coupled with a generally low level of activity in the villages during the day and with customary restrictions on women's movement. Life for a woman in these sleepy communities could be monotonous, uneventful, isolated and difficult.

The spatial arrangement of households in the three villages followed closely the general pattern of most West Bank highland villages. Located on semi-arid and rather rocky terrain, villages lost as little arable land as possible by building homes on hilltops, and by leaving plains, wadis and hillsides free for agricultural purposes. Older, limestone houses tended to cluster in the centre of the villages, while newer, cement-brick dwellings lay scattered around the periphery. The new houses tended to be occupied by younger couples, who had moved out of the extended family household to establish independent lives. The number of nuclear households in these villages appeared to be growing.

Population and Household Organisation

All three villages were relatively small. The largest, populated by about 1400 people, followed by 600 for the second, dwarfed the meagre 250 in the third. Of the 336 households in the three villages, very few consisted of one person. Those who did live alone were usually very old: either unmarried women, or women whose husband and children or next of kin were either dead or abroad seeking employment. Living alone is not valued by villagers but is considered the result of a crisis or catastrophe - an abnormal way of life. A few of the households were very large, the largest being composed of 18 members. The average household size was 6.5 members (Table 3.1).

TABLE 3.1

POPULATION OF THE THREE VILLAGES
GENERAL CHARACTERISTICS

	Village 1	Village 2	Village 3	Total
Population	228	586	1374	2188
Households	36	98	202	336
Average household size	6.3	6	6.8	6.5
Smallest household	1	1	1	3
Largest household	13	13	18	44

Of the total number of households, a surprising 70 per cent were occupied by nuclear families. The rest were composed of the traditional extended families, which could include up to four generations. There were 41 households, 13 per cent, whose heads were women. Most of their husbands were abroad working, and their male children were too small to take over the responsibility of heading the family. A few husbands were serving prison sentences in Israeli jails. Some women were widowed.

The population of these villages was rather young; about 46 per cent were under 15 years old. Women constituted 51 per cent of the total population; women of childbearing age, between 15 and 49 years, constituted 22 per cent. The total number of married women and children, the priority groups and targets for health intervention, was thus about 68 per cent of the population. This is clearly a substantial proportion, and reinforces our argument for locating these two groups at the centre of our investigation. Coupled with the biological fact of higher risk of disease and death among members of these two categories, in addition to gender-related, socially determined health and other risks, this percentage eliminates any concern about undue bias in investigating only women and their children's needs and concerns (Chart 3.1 and Table 3.2).

Table 3.2 (see below, page 49) indicates that age distribution among the population of the three villages does not follow the normal distribution of a model stable population. The variations appear more clearly if the observed population is compared with a model stable one of approximately the same growth rate (Chart 3.2) (3). First, there seem to be fewer female children within the 0-3 years age category than might have been expected, especially compared with the male population in the same age category. Although this discrepancy between the sexes may be due entirely to chance, given the small population we are dealing with, it may nevertheless suggest preferential treatment of male children. Infant mortality data suggests female mortality as

CHART 3.1

The Population Pyramid

The Three Villages

Age group in years

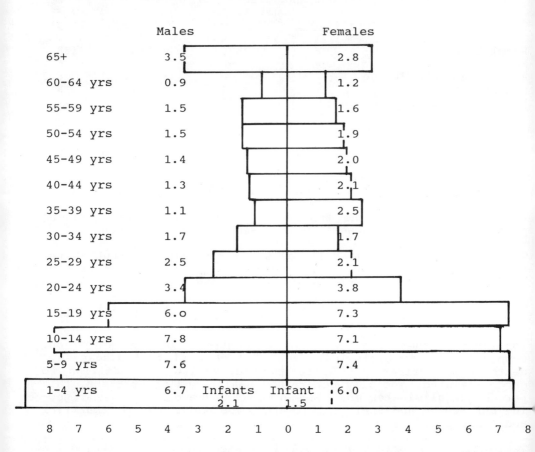

	Males	Females
65+	3.5	2.8
60-64 yrs	0.9	1.2
55-59 yrs	1.5	1.6
50-54 yrs	1.5	1.9
45-49 yrs	1.4	2.0
40-44 yrs	1.3	2.1
35-39 yrs	1.1	2.5
30-34 yrs	1.7	1.7
25-29 yrs	2.5	2.1
20-24 yrs	3.4	3.8
15-19 yrs	6.0	7.3
10-14 yrs	7.8	7.1
5-9 yrs	7.6	7.4
1-4 yrs	6.7	6.0

Infants Infant
  2.1   1.5

8   7   6   5   4   3   2   1   0   1   2   3   4   5   6   7   8

Percentage of Total Population

Total Population: 2188   Total Households: 336
Males as a Percentage of Total Population: 49%
Females as a Percentage of Total Population: 51%

being higher than male, and nutritional assessment shows better
overall nutrition for boys than for girls. Our observation also
showed differential attitudes and behaviour in favour of boys.
Initial examination of the health parameters thus alerts us to
the need for keeping this particular line of investigation open,
without elaborating or attempting to hypothesise on possible
causation.

TABLE 3.2

POPULATION BY AGE AND SEX

| Age in Years | Percentage of Total | | |
	Males	Females	Total
0-4	8.8	7.5	16.3
5-9	7.6	7.4	15.0
10-14	7.8	7.1	14.9
15-19	6.0	7.3	13.3
20-24	3.4	3.8	7.2
25-29	2.5	2.9	5.4
30-34	1.7	1.7	3.4
35-39	1.1	2.5	3.6
40-44	1.3	2.1	3.4
45-49	1.4	2.0	3.4
50-54	1.5	1.9	3.4
55-59	1.5	1.6	3.1
60-64	0.9	1.2	2.1
65 and over	3.5	2.8	6.4
Total	49.0	51.0	100.0
Children under 15	24.2	22.0	46.2
Women of childbearing age (between 15 and 49)		22.3	
Women of childbearing age and children under 15			68.5

Chart 3.2 also indicates a disproportionate number of people over
65 years old. This may be due to people in this category's
overestimation of their ages, especially given that it is mostly
composed of illiterates. This raises the question of the general
accuracy of age reporting within the total population. Our
assessment is that those who were under 35 to 40 years old seemed
to have reported their ages fairly accurately; their reporting
was based on concrete information relating to the year, and
sometimes the month of their birth; and based on birth certificates and Israeli identity cards. Those over 40 tended to rely
on significant village or national events to date their birth
year (such as the year of the snow, or the year of the catastrophe; that is, the 1948 Arab-Israeli war, and so on), if at all.

A third point of interest revealed by Chart 3.2 is the slightly
inflated proportion of children under 15 years old, and the

substantially reduced proportion of persons between the ages of
20 and about 45.   This appears to hold true for both sexes,
although it affects the male population to a larger extent than
the female.   Chart 3.3, a simple graphic description of the
male/female ratio of the population, provides additional
information. What it basically indicates is an imbalance between
the proportions of males and females currently living in the
three villages.   Males, particularly males 30 to 44 years old,
are virtually absent.   The same pattern of disproportion between
male and female population of the age category 0 to 4 years
appears again here, in reverse, but perhaps more clearly.

The information revealed by Charts 3.2 and 3.3 suggests that the
population is not a closed one.   Outmigration could probably
explain this particular pattern.   There appears to be a tendency
towards outmigration from the village in early adult life, which
increasingly affects both sexes.   A possible explanation for the
observed, lower than expected, proportion of females between the
ages of 15 and 34 is that younger couples are increasingly opting
to outmigrate as families; as opposed to the older pattern where
the husband left his wife and children in the village while he
sought work abroad.   In 1981, 83, or 78 per cent, of all married
emigrant sons of household heads had their wives and children
living with them abroad.   Information collected throughout the
survey, and various discussions on the subject tend to support
outmigration as an explanation.   An alternative, and not mutually
exclusive, explanation could be that because of the substantial
deficit in the number of marriageable young men, village women
were simply being married outside the village.   The deficit in
the number of women within the younger adult category may reflect
a changing pattern of marriage, from intra-village to inter-
village and village-town.   This explanation, however, is not
supported by our informants, who tended to believe that entire
family outmigration had been increasing since the mid-1970s.

Perhaps the increasing political instability and economic
hardships in the area as a whole could explain the tendency
towards outmigration (4).   In recent years, however, this
tendency has been thwarted because Palestinians seeking employment abroad, mostly in the Arab world, have been facing increasing difficulties in finding and retaining jobs in the Arab
countries (Table 3.3).   The economic recession in the Gulf
states, coupled with a variety of political events, is today
making the average Palestinian, and the villagers no less than
others, more reluctant to make the outward move towards the Arab
world (5).   This is true in spite of the hardships that must be
withstood under Israeli military rule and the fluctuating Israeli
market for wage labour.

CHART 3.2

Comparison of observed age distribution with
model stage age distribution

Female _____

Male - - - - - - - - - - -

Observed
 Stable

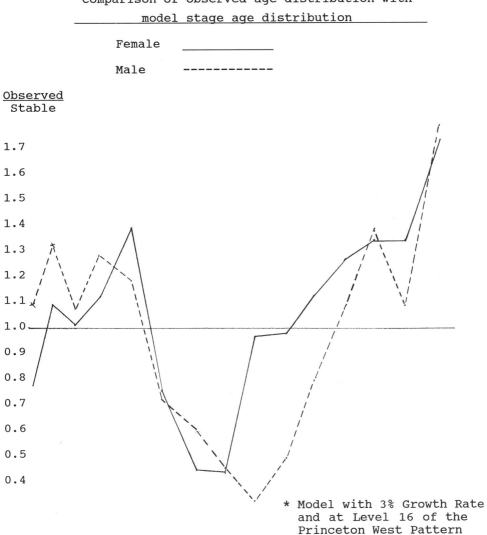

1.7

1.6

1.5

1.4

1.3

1.2

1.1

1.0

0.9

0.8

0.7

0.6

0.5

0.4

* Model with 3% Growth Rate
   and at Level 16 of the
   Princeton West Pattern

0-4   10-14   20-24   30-34   40-44   50-54   60-64   65+

Age in years

CHART 3.3

<u>Sex Ratio (Male/Female)</u>

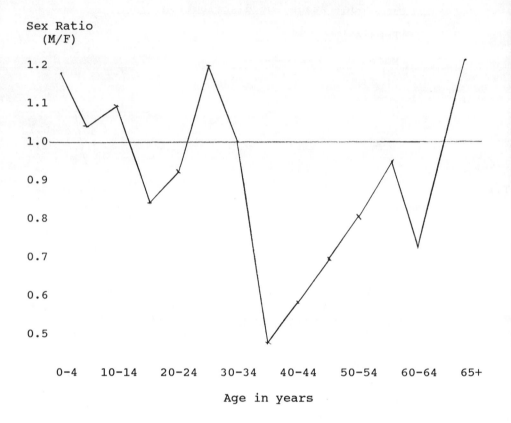

Sex Ratio
  (M/F)

TABLE 3.3

DISTRIBUTION OF ADULT MALE MIGRANTS FROM THE THREE VILLAGES
BY COUNTRY OF RESIDENCE

(sons of heads of households only)

Location	Percentage of total migrants
Jordan	44
Other Arab Countries	38
USA	8
Latin America	5
Germany	2
Eastern Europe	3
Total	100
Total migrants	169

Though a tendency towards outmigration is visible, the reverse does not appear to occur much; migration into the three villages is minimal. This is quite understandable, given a village economy that cannot even support the existing inhabitants, as we shall discuss later. For all practical purposes, it appears that the primary means through which heterogeneity in population composition is achieved is through the acquisition of wives from outside the village. Of 272 married women of childbearing age interviewed, 63, or 23 per cent, were born and raised in villages other than where they eventually settled in marriage. This is not an insignificant proportion.

In sum, though the villages are organised and divided around the traditional Hamula (clan or extended family structure), they remain nevertheless and to a significant extent, a homogeneous population, closed to immigration, but with a shifting population composition. This composition appears determined to a large extent by work opportunities available abroad in the Arab world and, therefore, by political and economic factors influencing these opportunities.

A quick comparison of Tables 3.4 and 3.5 indicates that, on the whole, our three villages do not compare favourably with the national averages for amenities despite a widespread belief that the general living conditions in the Ramallah District villages are superior to those of other districts. Although the average household is slightly smaller than the West Bank average (6.5 versus 6.9), 58 per cent of the three villages' families live in dwellings composed of two rooms or less, while 53 per cent of West Bank village households live in two rooms or less. The crowding rate, then, is about the same for both. Only 10 per cent of our village households have a running water supply, compared to a West Bank average of 29.6 per cent. This may be less a reflection of the communities' awareness of the importance of running water, than a consequence of the Israeli military government's control of water sources (8).

TABLE 3.4

SELECTED HOUSEHOLD CHARACTERISTICS AND FACILITIES
THE THREE VILLAGES

Total households   336
Average household size (no. members)   6.5
Average rooms per household   2.7

Features	Number	Percentage
Families in two rooms or less	192	57
Families in three rooms or less	259	77
Households with kitchens	232	69
Households with internal latrines	50	15
Households with external latrines	191	57
Households with no latrines	95	28
Total	336	100
Households with internal piped water supply connected to cistern	43	13
Households with internal piped water connected to municipal supply	14	4
Households with municipal water supply but no internal pipes	20	6
Households with cisterns and no internal pipes	212	63
Households with other sources of water (neighbour's well, spring, purchased)	47	14
Total	336	100
Households with around-the-clock electricity supply	316	94

TABLE 3.5

SELECTED HOUSEHOLD CHARACTERISTICS AND FACILITIES
WEST BANK VILLAGES, 1980-1981

Average household size (no. persons)   6.9 (6)
Households with two rooms or less   53.0% (6)
Households with electricity around the clock 29.6% (7)
Households with toilet facilities   78.5% (7)
Households with running water   29.3% (7)

Seventy-two per cent of our village households have toilet
facilities, which is less than the West Bank average of 78 per
cent.   In contrast, however, 94 per cent of our village households have electricity around the clock, compared with an average
of 29.6 per cent.   Like the provision of running water, the
connection of villages to the national electrical grid is under
the control of the Israeli military, and subject to political
considerations.   What this quick comparison indicates is that
living conditions, as expressed by the presence or absence of the
above-mentioned facilities, are to a substantial extent determined, not only by the availability of cash, or the presence of a
collective spirit that encourages communal investments, but also
by the particular policies that the military occupier wishes to
pursue at a particular point in time.   Development project
committees have existed in the villages for some time, with the
purpose of overseeing the implementation of needed service
projects.   They have, for example, succeeded in bringing
electricity to the villages, opening an internal network of roads
and, in one of them, set out to fix up the village cemetery.   Two
of these committees continue to struggle with the Israeli
military to obtain a permit to connect the villages with a
running water supply.   In the three villages, the effects of
occupation policies on the availability of selected facilities in
households are reflected in a mixed record of achievements.

In terms of ownership of household amenities, especially
electrical items, our villages seemed to fare quite well,
especially considering that around-the-clock electrical current
was a recent phenomenon in 1981.   The largest village had been
connected to the national grid just months before we first began
our work there.   Before then some well-to-do members of the
communities had purchased electrical generators and turned them
into business enterprises.   They sold electrical current to
individual households for regular monthly payments.   But even
then, televisions were infiltrating the communities, who were
deeply appreciative of this sudden contact with the outside
world, especially Egyptian soap operas.   By 1981, 199 families,
or 59 per cent, of the total households, owned radios; 207, or 62
per cent, gas ranges; 18, or 5.4 per cent, washing machines; and
16, or 4.8 per cent, cars (Table 3.6).   Cars were considered good
investments; not only could they be used for private purposes,
but also for earning income by providing transportation services
to community members, especially at night, when almost all
traffic activity comes to a halt.

TABLE 3.6

OWNERSHIP OF SELECTED HOUSEHOLD AMENITIES
THE THREE VILLAGES

Amenity	Number of households	Percentage of total
Radio	199	59.0
Television	207	62.0
Refrigerator	123	37.0
Gas Range	214	64.0
Washing Machine	18	5.4
Car	16	4.8
Total households	336	

The majority of families, except a few of the refugee families in
the medium-sized village, own land. Even some of these refugee
families have succeeded in purchasing land from the original
village inhabitants. Around 87 per cent, or 272 households,
cultivate at least part of the land they own, the rest of the
land is noncultivable. But (as Salim Tamari noted, while
investigating the impact of wage labour on the peasant family
farm in our large-sized village), land is no longer a criterion
for wealth (9). The majority of land owned appeared to be small
and medium-sized by West Bank highland standards. In addition,
14 households, or 4 per cent, owned cultivable land in villages
other than their own (Table 3.7).

TABLE 3.7

OWNERSHIP OF CULTIVABLE LAND BY LOCATION

Land ownership	Village 1		Village 2		Village 3		Total	
	no.	%age	no.	%age	no.	%age	no.	%age
Within the immediate vicinity of dwelling	28	78	70	71	172	85	270	80
Away from dwelling but in the village	28	78	52	52	169	84	249	74
In another village	3	8	7	7	4	2	14	4
Total ownership	33	92	73	74	186	92	292	87
Total households	36		98		202		336	

With cultivation being totally dependent on rain for irrigation,
and with a largely hilly and at times rocky terrain, agricultural production is limited to crops that can withstand the
harshness of the soil and the limited supply of water. Olives
are by far the most important harvest in these communities that
lie in the heart of olive country; followed by a range of fruits
(figs, plums, almonds, and grapes), vegetables, pulses, and
wheat. About 23 per cent, or 111 households, reported selling
their produce, mostly olives and olive oil, and some fruits. The

rest used the produce entirely for family consumption (Table 3.8).

TABLE 3.8

CULTIVATION BY HOUSEHOLD AND TYPE OF PRODUCE
THE THREE VILLAGES

	Number of households	Percentage of total
Households that cultivate land	292	100
Type of produce		
Olives	261	89
Fruits	248	84
Vegetables	222	76
Pulses	180	62
Wheat	88	30

Though 196, or 59 per cent, of households keep animals, only five, or 2 per cent, do so as a means of subsidising the family income. One of those households owns the only 60 cows found in the three villages. In this case, the household head indicated that animal husbandry was his major means of earning income for his family. The other four households owned the bulk of the communities' sheep and goats. The heads of those households, too, said that animal ownership was a major, although not exclusive, income-generating activity (Table 3.9). The large majority of households utilised animals as a means to supplement the family diet, or to help in agricultural work (as with donkeys), rather than for income-generating or exchange purposes.

TABLE 3.9

ANIMAL OWNERSHIP AND FATE OF PRODUCE BY HOUSEHOLD AND TYPE
THE THREE VILLAGES

Animal ownership	Number of families	Percentage of total
Total ownership - all animals	196	59
Donkeys	147	44
Goats	143	43
Chicken	120	36
Sheep	34	10
Pigeons	22	7
Total households	336	
Fate of produce		
Used for family consumption	191	97
Sold	5	3
Total families	196	

Changing Work Patterns

One of the most remarkable features of life in these peasant
communities is the dramatic changes that have occurred since the
1967 Arab-Israeli war, and the fall of the West Bank under
Israeli military rule (10). Those changes, which appear to have
affected almost every aspect of life, were most strongly
emphasised by the older generations. As was the case with the
majority of villages in the West Bank, before 1967 these
communities relied on agriculture as the major source of income.
According to Sarah Graham-Brown, in the 1930s and 1940s, about 70
per cent of the area's population gained their livelihood from
agriculture (11). Wage labour existed; but mostly as a supplement to incomes generated from agricultural pursuits. Van
Arkadie described the general characteristics of the West Bank at
the time. According to Van Arkadie, under Jordanian rule the
economy of the West Bank was largely based on agriculture, with a
diversified output. Agriculture provided jobs for almost one
half of the labour force; but the agricultural workforce was
underemployed, and a high rate of open unemployment prevailed
(12). In our communities, the problem of underemployment was
partially alleviated by emigration to the Arab world in search of
work, and migration east to what was then the capital, Amman.
Some even managed to reach Latin America. Most emigration was
limited to men, who tended to leave their wives and children in
the village, under the care of the extended family. Others
worked as agricultural labourers in nearby villages, or sought
work in construction and the service sector in West Bank towns.
In all, the economy in these communities was based on agriculture; the majority owned and cultivated their land as a major
source of income, and as a way of life.

By 1981, however, work patterns had changed considerably, at
least partially as a result of the integration of the West Bank
into the Israeli labour market. While no one knows the exact
nature of the economy of these villages from the 1930s onward,
and therefore the nature of their occupational structure, one
could assume that these do not differ substantially from the
national picture. And if village occupational structure can be
taken as a measure of change, then the fact that only 48 households, or 14 per cent, derived their major income from agriculture in 1981 indicates a dramatic change from agriculture to
wage labour (Table 3.10). Table 3.10 also indicates that, of
the total active workers, 236, or 70 per cent, were unskilled or
semi-skilled wage labourers. There was a larger proportion of
semi-skilled labourers in village 3 than the other two and,
likewise, a slightly larger number of farmers. What is clear,
however, is that overall, the majority of households in the three
villages derived incomes from wage labour. Although the overall
figures for unemployment were high, 16 per cent, they should be
read with particular caution. This is because employment in
Israel is casual and often illegal.

TABLE 3.10

OCCUPATION BY TYPE (BOTH SEXES)

Occupation type	Village 1 no.	Village 1 %age	Village 2 no.	Village 2 %age	Village 3 no.	Village 3 %age	Total no.	Total %age
Unskilled labourers	20	47	36	45	64	30	120	36
Semi-skilled	10	23	21	26	85	39	116	34
Farmers	5	12	9	11	35	16	48	14
White collar workers	5	12	7	9	12	6	24	7
Self-employment	3	6	7	9	20	9	30	9
Total workers	43	100	80	100	216	100	338	100
Total workforce	47		98		257		401	
Unemployment of total workforce	4	9	18	18	41	16	63	16
Women workers of total workforce	6	13	8	8	17	7	31	8
Total population	228		586		1374		2188	
Workforce as percentage of total population		20		17		19		18

Those villagers who work in Israel retain their work only for a limited period of time. Once the particular work that has been contracted for is completed, the workers return to their villages and begin the search for new opportunities. Thus, the casual and interrupted nature of their work means that the level of unemployment at any given moment is not a reliable indicator of their overall level of employment year round. Indeed, it is doubtful that any member of these communities who was willing to work as wage labourer would not have found employment in Israel for a good part of the year in 1981.

TABLE 3.11

EMPLOYMENT BY LOCATION OF WORK

Work location	Village 1 no.	Village 1 %age	Village 2 no.	Village 2 %age	Village 3 no.	Village 3 %age	Total no.	Total %age
Home village	5	12	22	27	83	39	117	33
West Bank	28	68	47	59	55	26	130	39
Israel	8	20	11	14	76	35	95	28
Total	41	100	80	100	214	100	335	100

Thus agriculture as the economic base of these three communities in 1981 was no longer able to provide either the needed employ-ment, or sufficient resources for the reproduction of the old system. The presence of the tough competition of wage labour in the West Bank, Israel, and abroad after 1967 meant that, as

Tamari has noted, many family farms were marginalised and
increasingly neglected (13). By 1981, only 117 or 33 per cent of
the total number of people employed found work in their village
(Table 3.11). The rest sought and found employment as wage
labourers in both the West Bank and Israel. It should be borne
in mind that the figure of 95 or 28 per cent of the total listed
for workers in Israel most likely represents an underestimation
of the real figures. If one takes into consideration the numbers
listed as unemployed, assuming that the majority of those were
"caught" by the survey at a time when their work was temporarily
interrupted because of its casual nature, then the more likely
figure of about 40 per cent employment in Israel emerges. But
even then the proportion employed in Israel from village 3 was
more than that of the other two villages. The data obtained on
emigrants (Table 3.12) may offer an explanation.

TABLE 3.12

EMIGRANTS BY VILLAGE
SONS OF HEADS OF HOUSEHOLDS ONLY

Emigrants	Village 1		Village 2		Village 3		Total	
	no.	%age	no.	%age	no.	%age	no.	%age
Emigrant students	2	14	2	3	11	15	15	9
Emigrant workers	12	86	78	97	64	85	154	91
Total emigrant sons	14	100	80	100	75	100	169	100
Emigrant sons of total emigrants in villages	14	8	80	47	75	44	169	100
Households with one or more emigrants	6	17	49	50	44	22	99	30
Total village population	228	100	586	100	1374	100	2188	100

Table 3.12 indicates that village 2 emigrants are over-represent-
ed, especially when the village total population is taken into
consideration. Despite the fact that village 3, for instance, is
over twice the size of village 2, the latter accounted for 47 per
cent of the total emigrant sons of the three villages. Likewise,
50 per cent of village 2 households had one or more emigrants
abroad, while village 3 and village 1 had 22 and 17 per cent,
respectively. This information suggests that, faced with the
options of working in Israel or abroad, village 2 members chose
the latter option, perhaps due to better contacts and stronger
ties with their family members abroad.

The post-1967 period presented the peasant households in our
communities with new and alternative forms of labour and new
sources of wealth. Our peasant households appear to have been
quick in seizing on the new opportunities and combining resources
from various labour activities, as has happened elsewhere, in,
for example, the South African household (14). Yet, until today,
family farms, though increasingly marginalised, are still

considered an important source of income. Olive farming is still very much alive, as can easily be witnessed in autumn. The olive harvest is a time when the entire family, even those who work in Israel, participate; it is profitable enough to justify this. It is also a time of great festivity. As Tamari has put it:

> Land to the peasant - even to the "proletarianised peasant" of the West Bank - is not primarily real estate ... but security ... it supplements his cash earnings from wage labour... "the land is always there" in case he is laid off from work or is compelled to remain unemployed for a long period in search of work ... the family farm constitutes the worker's physical and symbolic link with his immediate community, and hence with peasant culture in general (15).

Whether these physical and symbolic links to the land will prove strong enough to offset the pressures and temptations of wage labour in Israel and abroad, however, remains to be seen. More importantly, if this new dependence on a mix of migrant and wage labour income and agricultural returns became problematic, it is not clear whether a retreat into agricultural production - in case of need - would still be feasible.

The initial disruption of the local economy and therefore the social structure appeared to have been partially positive in that the poorly paid agricultural labour reserve and others working in the service sector were suddenly faced with the opportunity for employment in Israel. Because of the difference in the two economies, wages which were low by Israeli standards were excellent in terms of purchasing power on the West Bank. Since the mid-1970s, however, there has been a levelling of the two economies; at this stage, Palestinians working in Israel face increasing difficulty in making ends meet.

The Educational Picture

The educational level in the three communities has also been undergoing rapid changes. These, in turn, have imparted their effects on attitudes and practices and the peasant way of life in general. Education is highly valued by Palestinians everywhere. 'Il-'lm mal' ('education is money'), the saying goes. One important lesson Palestinians have learned in recent history is that education is a means of survival. To Palestinians in the diaspora, education has been substituted for land as a means of security and of social and economic mobility. And, in a sense, educational attainment has come to symbolise the continuing refusal of Palestinians to part with their cultural identity. In the Israeli-occupied territories, schools and universities have become symbols of resistance and of the re-emergence of Palestinian national and cultural identity, as well as centres of learning. With the threat of land confiscation and expulsion being constantly felt, Palestinians under occupation have also opted for educational attainment as a protection against future

disasters.   Because of these factors and others, the record of
educational attainment among Palestinians has been one of
systematic improvement over the last three decades (17).   Yet,
despite these improvements, substantial discrepancies between the
educational levels of the various population categories persist,
most notably between the sexes in rural areas (18).

TABLE 3.13

LITERACY OVER THE AGE OF 15 YEARS BY SEX
THE THREE VILLAGES

		Literacy Status				Total	
Age group	Males		Females		Both sexes		population	
	no.	%age	no.	%age	no.	%age	no.	%age
15-24	196	95	200	83	396	89	446	100
25-34	84	93	45	54	129	74	174	100
35-44	43	81	15	15	58	38	151	100
45-54	37	59	4	5	41	29	144	100
55 and above	55	44	1	1	56	23	249	100
Literacy under 35	280	95	245	76	525	85		
Literacy over 35	135	56	20	7	155	29		
Total literacy	415	77	265	42	680	58		
Total population over 15	538		626		1164			

The three villages exhibit similar patterns of both improvement
over time and inequality between the sexes.   Table 3.13 is a
breakdown of the literacy rates by age categories and sex.
Seventy-seven per cent of the total adult male population was
found literate; illiteracy was concentrated among those 45 years
of age or older, and gradually diminished with decreasing age.
Much more dramatic is the pattern for women.   Only 42 per cent of
the women were found literate, a percentage that lags considerably behind that of males.   The pattern of increased literacy rate
with decreasing age is much sharper than for males, indicating a
more rapid and more recent change in literacy among women.   The
literacy rate among women 55 years of age or over was 1 per cent,
while that of those in the 15-24-year-old age group was 83 per
cent.   The literacy rate among those under 35 was 76 per cent;
that of those who were 35 years of age or older was 7 per cent.
Illiteracy among women, then, was concentrated most among the
older generation; but it persisted as a phenomenon of substantial
proportions, even among women in their twenties.

TABLE 3.14

EDUCATIONAL ATTAINMENT BY SEX AND LEVEL
AGES 15 YEARS AND OVER
THE THREE VILLAGES

Years of schooling	Educational Attainment					
	Males		Females		Total	
	no.	%age	no.	%age	no.	%age
None	137	25	328	52	465	40
1-6	144	27	165	26	309	26
7-12	218	41	132	21	350	30
13 years and more	39	7	6	1	45	4
Total population	538	100	631	100	1169	100

Formal education data reveals basically the same patterns. Note that 25 per cent of the males indicated that they had no formal education at all, even though 33 per cent reported themselves literate. This is because, especially among older men, literacy is not only a function of formal schooling, but also of studying the Kur'an (the Muslim holy book). For women, the trend is opposite that of men. Although 52 per cent reported no formal schooling, 58 per cent indicated that they could neither read nor write. A few years of schooling, if coupled with early marriage and an ensuing lack of exposure to written material, frequently results in the loss of literacy. This was clearly the case with some of the women interviewed here. Although we attempted to test the ease with which women who reported themselves as literate could read the newspaper, we did not do so in a systematic and controlled fashion. But the initial evidence suggests that literacy, as estimated by the number of completed years of schooling, may not be an adequate measure of the individual's ability to read and write. This appears to be the case mostly with individuals who completed only the first few years of primary schooling, and especially with women.

TABLE 3.15

SCHOOL ENROLLMENT BY AGE AND SEX
THE THREE VILLAGES

Age group in years	Years of schooling	School Enrollment						age group	
		Males		Females		Total			
		no.	%age	no.	%age	no.	%age	no.	%age
7-12	1-6	196	99	176	96	374	97	384	100
13-15	7-9	91	87	82	81	173	84	206	100
16-18	10 & more	55	69	46	46	101	56	181	100
Total enrollment		342	89	306	79	648	84	771	100
Total age groups		384	100	387	100	771	100		

TABLE 3.16

FEMALE ENROLLMENT IN SCHOOLS BY AGE
THE THREE VILLAGES

Age group in years	Female enrollment		Both sexes	
	no.	%age	no.	%age
7-12	178	48	374	100
13-15	82	47	173	100
16-18	46	46	101	100
Total female enrollment	306	47	648	100
Total school population			771	100
Total number of females	387	50		

Figures for the enrollment of school-age children also show the pattern of continued improvement in educational attainment over time. A comparison of Tables 3.14 and 3.15 indicates that while 30 per cent of the adult population had reached the 7-12 years of schooling level or over, 84 per cent of the 13-15-year-olds were enrolled in the 7-9 years level (preparatory cycle) and 56 per cent of the 16-18 year olds were enrolled in the 10-12 years level (secondary cycle). The figures are more pronounced for females. Eighty-one and 46 per cent of school-age girls were enrolled in the preparatory and secondary cycles respectively; while only 21 per cent of adult women had reached the 7-12 years level. The ratios between male and female school enrollment provides additional evidence that the educational attainment of girls, even at the high school or secondary level, is almost equal to that of boys (Table 3.16). The sex ratios for school enrollment also seem to compare favourably with both those for the Ramallah District and those of the West Bank as a whole (Table 3.17). It should be borne in mind that enrollment figures for the Ramallah District and the West Bank include figures for both rural areas and towns. Thus the data strongly suggests that, in these three villages, illiteracy and lack of education among women is a rapidly disappearing phenomenon.

TABLE 3.17

FEMALE ENROLLMENT IN SCHOOLS BY LEVEL AND AREA (19)
RAMALLAH DISTRICT AND THE WEST BANK, 1980-81

Level	Ramallah District	West Bank
Primary (6 years)	48.3%	47.2%
Preparatory (3 years)	44.1%	42.6%
Secondary (3 years)	41.0%	37.4%

Whether inequalities between rural and urban areas are also being reduced with time is much more difficult to ascertain. The available information regarding education in the West Bank tends to be unreliable. In addition, it is usually presented without the necessary breakdown by rural or urban locality. Information is available, however, concerning the educational level in other villages and other districts, and the village of Zbeidat may be of special interest. Zbeidat is a peasant community located in the Jordan Valley region, known to be the most underdeveloped and least accessible of all the regions of the West Bank. A survey conducted in that village in 1980 revealed that the majority of adult women and school-age girls were illiterate (20). Another survey of seven villages in the same region in 1983 also revealed that the majority of women over the age of 15 were illiterate (21).

Educational attainment, especially among women, appeared to be dependent on at least four factors: the degree to which agriculture forms the economic base of rural communities; the nature of the agricultural cycle; the accessibility of schooling and educational opportunities; and the state of consciousness regarding education within communities.

In the mid-1970s, Zbeidat was in the process of disintegration because of the effects of Israeli military government confiscation of about half its most fertile land. The village was revived in the late 1970s with the introduction of drip irrigation techniques in farming. The results were an intensification of agriculture; several-fold increases in yields; the restoration of farming as the economic base of the community; and the general revitalisation of the village. Agricultural intensification and increased yields also meant that the labour of both women and children became much more important, especially in weeding and picking, which do not lend themselves to mechanisation. For men, drip technology meant a reduction in the total amount of labour needed to perform various agricultural activities. This resulted in the release of men, at least for part of the year, to work as wage labourers in the nearby Israeli settlements erected on the village's confiscated land (22). Thus the effects of new technology on the division of labour was that the men's workload was reduced and the women and children's workload increased.

The agricultural cycle in Zbeidat did not lend itself to encouraging educational attainment among the population. Women and children especially were preoccupied with intensive weeding, picking, and other activities for at least eight months of the year. The resting period, moreover, coincided with the time schools close down for the summer holidays. That the majority of boys in Zbeidat were attending school while the majority of girls were not was also heavily influenced by the community's access to educational establishments. There were no schools of any sort in Zbeidat in 1980; boys had to walk a distance of three kilometres on the main road in order to reach the school in a nearby village. Because of relatively strong kinship and family ties, and the customary restrictions on women's and girls' movement, the absence of schools in the village was an additional stumbling block to the girls' education. These factors, coupled with the fact that until recently Zbeidat's exposure to the outside world and its values was extremely limited, make the literacy and education picture for women and girls in this community, quite understandably, poor.

These factors influenced the educational picture of women in the Ramallah District villages in very different ways. Wage labour opportunities in Israel and abroad marginalised agriculture to the extent that very few households were fully dependent on family farms as a primary source of income. The agricultural cycle, in addition, was mostly shaped by the requirements of olive farming and, to a lesser extent, fruit farming. Both are dependent on rainfall and do not require irrigation. Other than ploughing and picking, farming activities remain at a minimum throughout most of the year. Although the entire family participated in olive picking during the autumn, the yield of other fruits was generally not high enough to warrant the labour of all family members. Thus it was usually women, and sometimes children and men, who picked and prepared fruits either for sale or for family consumption. The requirements for labour were not high enough to warrant pulling potential students out of school on a permanent basis. When their labour was required, as with olive picking, children were pulled out of school temporarily, for periods that did not exceed a few weeks. Moreover, olive picking in the West Bank highlands is a national event; and it is common for schools and universities to close down temporarily in order to meet the requirements for labour at a national level. While it may be true that in the Ramallah District communities, work opportunities in Israel and abroad meant an increase in women's workload, and their adoption of specific agricultural tasks previously the domain of men, the new division of labour did not increase the women's workload to the extent that it required the continuous additional support of child labour.

The tradition of literacy and education in the three Ramallah District villages had been a reasonably long one, dating back to the early 1950s, when the first state-run primary schools were established. This holds true for men, and to some extent for women as well. By the 1960s, preparatory school education became accessible, although even today, secondary schooling has to be sought in Birzeit or Ramallah. Birzeit is three kilometres away from the nearest village and about eight kilometres from the farthest. These distances can probably explain the sharp drop in school attendance once the secondary level is reached, among both boys and girls, but affecting girls to a greater extent (Table 3.15). Yet despite the lack of access and the problems for girls in moving from one village to another, a substantial proportion of students reach the secondary school level. This seemed to be associated with the communities' attitude towards education and their degree of exposure to the outside world. These communities lie literally next door to Birzeit University, and in the heart of the educational and intellectual centre of the West Bank. The increased value of education for both sexes, and the linking of education to the general national struggle are two messages continually reinforced by the presence of Birzeit University in the midst of these rural communities. These messages are bound

to have affected the consciousness of the surrounding people,
both in the ways they value education and their recognition of
the need for equality between the sexes.

Although it may be true that class and gender inequalities in
educational opportunities are being reduced in the West Bank
today, as some Palestinians would like to think, comparison
between the actual situations in two regions (the Ramallah and
Jordan Valley Districts) does alert us that this improvement may
not be universally applicable. Accessibility and attitudes
towards education are clearly important factors affecting both
the extent and the rapidity of the reduction in inequalities.
Yet those do not operate in a vacuum, but within the context of
the nature of production and the division of labour in specific
social settings.

NOTES

1. The water problem in the occupied territories is substan-
    tial. Since 1967, Israel has taken over the control of the
    water sources of the area.   The policy of all Israeli
    governments since then has been a consistent denial of
    equal access to water resources to Palestinians.   The
    Israeli Water Law of 1959 stipulates that the water
    resources in the State of Israel are public property, and
    forms the foundation for denial of access to irrigation
    water as well as water for domestic consumption to Pales-
    tinians.   By 1983, one third of the pre-1967 annual water
    consumption of Israel originated in the rainfall over the
    Western slopes of the West Bank and was drawn by drilling
    inside pre-1967 Israel proper. Thus the denial of the right
    of Palestinians to utilise their water sources is seen as a
    means for Israel to fulfil its water needs.   For further
    information, see Economic Activity and Access to National
    Resources: Legal Restrictions on Access to Land and Water
    in Israel, Paper prepared for the International Conference
    on the Question of Palestine by a Consultant, at the request
    of the Preparatory Committee, United Nations document
    A/CONF.114/6, 20 June 1983, pp. 16-21.   The consequences of
    such a policy are many, but one of them is the problem of
    unavailability of safe and sufficient quantities of water in
    rural areas.   In 1982, according to the Central Bureau of
    Statistics' Statistical Abstracts of Israel, Jerusalem,
    1983, only 29% of rural households in the West Bank were
    provided with a running water supply. The problem of two of
    the three villages that were the subject of this investiga-
    tion was that with the help of a United States aid agency
    that provided the necessary finances for the project, the
    villages' leaders had been trying in vain to gain approval
    from the military government to execute a water project for
    four years, up until 1984.   Throughout this time there has
    been no response from the military government, neither
    positive nor negative - an effective blockade of the water
    project.   This problem is one among many examples of how
    political structures can influence, constrain and determine
    the limits of community development projects.

2. A community centre of sorts, which is usually collectively
    shared by members of the same Hamula for the purpose of
    family meetings, entertainment and the reception of guests.

3. Age distribution of a model stable population with a growth
    rate of 3% (the generally assumed growth rate for the
    Palestinian population in the West Bank) was obtained from
    Coale, A J & Demeny, P, Regional Model Life Tables and
    Stable Productions, Princeton University Press, Princeton,
    1966.

4. See, for instance, Yediot Aharonot, 'Tension between Arab
    and Jewish Workers', 13.8.84, English translation in Israel

Mirror no. 705-6, 17.10.84; Sefer, I, 'Israel's Economic Crisis and the West Bank', Hadashot, 12.8.84, English translation in Israel Mirror no 705-6, 17.10.84.

5. Ha'aretz, 'Palestinians return to the West Bank because of Arab Recession', 19.5.85, English translation in Israeli Mirror, no 705-6, 17.10.84.

6. Statistical Abstracts of Israel, Central Bureau of Statistics, Jerusalem, 1981, p. 742.

7. Statistical Abstracts of Israel, Central Bureau of Statistics, Jerusalem, 1982, pp. 746-47.

8. For further information regarding the impact of the water problem on West Bank agriculture and development, see Graham-Brown, S, 'The Economic Consequences of Occupation', in Aruri, op cit, pp. 170-179.

9. Tamari, S, 'Building Other People's Homes: The Palestinian Peasant's Household and Work in Israel', Journal of Palestine Studies, Vol XI, no 1, Autumn 1981, p. 57.

10. For a general account of the impact of Israeli occupation on Palestinian social structure, see Graham-Brown, S, 'Impact on the Social Structure of Palestinian Society', in Aruri, op cit, pp. 223-254. For an analysis of the way in which military occupation has particularly affected one of the three communities that are the subject of this investigation, see Tamari, S, 'Building other ...', op cit, pp. 31-65.

11. Graham-Brown in Aruri, op cit, p. 228.

12. Van Arkadie, B, 'Benefits and Burdens: A Report on the West Bank and Gaza Strip Economy since 1967', Carnegie Endowment for International Peace, New York, 1977, pp. 21-32.

13. Tamari, 'Building', op cit, p. 53.

14. Martin, W & Beittel, M, The Hidden Abode of Reproduction: Conceptualising Households in Southern Africa, Research Working Group Papers, Ferdinand Braudel Centre for the Study of Economies, Historical Systems and Civilization, State University of New York at Binghamton, Binghamton, New York, 1984.

15. Tamari, 'Building', op cit, p. 41.

16. For further information on the role of education among Palestinians, see Graham-Brown, S, Education, Repression, Liberation: Palestinians, World University Service, London, 1984.

17. Ibid.

18. It is almost impossible to locate reliable and published
     statistics regarding educational attainment by locality and
     sex.   Discussions on the subject with members of the
     literacy programme of Birzeit University, however, do seem
     to confirm that rural women are the least educated and most
     disadvantaged group among the population of the occupied
     territories.   Other research findings also seem to support
     this view.   See, for instance, Tamari & Giacaman, op cit,
     Part 1, p. 34.

19. <u>Quarterly Statistics of the Administered Territories</u>, Vol
     XI/I 1981, Appendix 3: 'Kindergartens and Schools in the
     Administered Territories 1980-81' (Hebrew only), cited in
     Graham-Brown, <u>Education</u>, op cit, p. 69.

20. Tamari & Giacaman, op cit, p. 34.

21. This information has been obtained from Alex Pollock, The
     Arab Thought Forum, Jerusalem, 1984.

22. Tamari & Giacaman, op cit, Part 1.

CHAPTER FOUR

SOME ASPECTS OF THE WORLD OF WOMEN

In these communities, as in other peasant communities, a variety
of constraints govern a woman's life. Biological reproduction is
understood as central to village life and continuity. It is
therefore a key factor in the determination of a woman's life
cycle. Her socialisation from her early years is geared
primarily towards her future role as a wife and mother. The
importance of procreation is used to justify the saying 'shajara
bala tamara qat'ha halal' ('it is lawful to hew down a tree which
does not bear fruit') (1). In general, those women who do not
bear children, and especially male children, are found in an
unhappy state. For children are the woman's support and future
security. It is ultimately through them, and not only through
marriage, that she gains her status in society. Although female
children are loved and cared for, it is the male children,
especially the male firstborn, who takes the primary position in
the hearts of parents. The roots of this preferential treatment
of male children lie within a preferential division of labour in
favour of men and all its legal, ideological and social ramifica-
tions. In these villages, as is the case with the occupied
territories at large, preferential treatment of males is governed
by a concrete set of institutions and relations: The family,
school, customs, religion and legal system all basically emit and
reinforce the notion of male moral and material superiority over
female. Men and women have divided tasks: men are responsible
for the maintenance of their wives and children; women for the
maintenance of the household. Women are considered weaker, and
men, considered stronger, are made the protectors and the
managers of their affairs (2). Women are only half as equal as
men in legal and financial matters. Inheritance laws discriminate against women so that they are allowed only half of the
share that is allotted to men (3). Even the documents necessary
to travel are forbidden to women without permission from the male
head of the family.

Thus, although the birth of a female child may bring joy and some
benefit to parents, these remain limited. For ultimately, since
they are considered the weaker sex, their benefits can turn into
burdens: they are thought to be potentially promiscuous and
insatiable by nature and therefore in constant need of being
controlled. Their domestic production is not highly valued.
They are seen to consume but hardly produce, for housework and

the type of agricultural tasks assigned to them are not highly valued or considered a source of income. This is becoming increasingly true today, with the increasing nuclearisation of families and mechanisation of housework. They are, in addition, a source of potential shame and dishonour; as they are considered weak, it is believed always possible that they will go astray. Between these potential problems and the primary role imposed on women - biological reproduction - the tendency is to marry them off as soon as feasible since their marriage reduces the costs of maintaining the family as well as the risks of dishonourable or shameful conduct. Family security, in contrast, is attached to the birth of a male child. It is he who is expected to take over financial, social and moral responsibility for the family. He will inherit family property (4) and ensure the continuity of the family name. He will ultimately provide for his parents' security in old age. In the occupied territories, no system of old age pension or social security exists, and therefore kinship relations perform the functions of a welfare state. Male children are thus frequently the only guarantee for the future.

The sexual division of labour interacts with and is compounded by the new division of labour in Palestinian society at large; Palestinians no longer own their means of production and are dependent on Israel for livelihood. But the effects of wage labour in Israel on the sexual division of labour are far from clear. On the one hand, production in the home subsidises the incomes Palestinian wage workers earn in Israel. Women's work in the home and in agriculture helps to maintain the family's livelihood and capacity for reproduction along with wage earnings (5). On the other hand, the opening-up of opportunities for women's labour outside the home could end up undermining the basis of home production. Women not only participate in agricultural tasks but also dry, can and pickle food, make soap and jams and grind wheat. Yet, despite the possible modification of the sexual division of labour that may come as a result of women's wage labour, it is difficult, indeed, to conceive achieving the liberation of Palestinian women in isolation of a radical change in existing political and economic relations. For a society such as that of the West Bank, which is ruled by military force and laws of segregation, cannot but continue to suffer from profound inequalities so long as the structures of its domination continue to exist. This is not meant to imply, however, that nothing can be done to improve women's conditions under military occupation; the progressive women's committees are achieving a great deal.

The consequences of unequal relations between men and women and the general debasement in women's status affect most aspects of women's life in these villages: they have unequal access to educational opportunities and work (as shown in Chapter Three); they suffer disparities in health status (see Chapter Seven); and their freedom is restricted. In short, women are unable to take control of their lives. The subjugation of women renders them subservient to husband, kin and society. It renders them and their needs invisible; since they are denied access to public

life, there is little knowledge of their problems or understanding of their needs. Their views on their communities' problems
are rarely solicited. The assumption is almost always that men
can adequately represent both men and women. Yet the sexual
division of labour and the resulting divide that separates the
two worlds are bound to have their effects on needs, problems,
priorities and aspirations.

Many of the villages' women were especially eager to discuss the
implications of the lack of the most basic services in their
communities. It was as if, once the opportunity presented
itself, the floodgates opened; now that their views were finally
solicited, they seized the chance to discuss their worries.
Problems concerning village development had been traditionally
considered the domain of men, not only by the members of these
communities, but also by aid agencies and the society at large.
Because of this, village development projects have been largely
determined by the priorities of men. Our field work suggested
that although at times the priorities of men and women are
similar, that is not always the case. For example, of a total of
226 women, 58 per cent listed lack of access to adequate
quantities of safe water as their major problem. They indicated
that piped water would be at the top of their development project
list. Thirty-two per cent felt that the lack of health services
was most important; 24 per cent wanted internal road improvements; and 16 per cent desired that secondary schooling be
available in their village. Although the men were not formally
interviewed, numerous discussions on the problems of village
services and on priorities for village projects took place.
These discussions invariably involved only men, including the
Mukhtars and other village notables. Their priorities put roads
at the top of the list; followed by water, schools, and health
facilities. Thus, although both men and women were living under
similar circumstances, the priorities of men, as expressed by the
village leadership, reflected the different needs of men and,
ultimately, the division of labour between the sexes. Men mostly
worked outside the village; roads were very important in
facilitating their transportation to work. Women worked in the
home; and water was the most crucial determinant of the amount
and difficulty of housework. Women were also responsible for
their children's health; so the presence of health facilities in
the village was of more importance to them than to the men.
Since men used mosques as a meeting place, they frequently
discussed mosques as possible development projects. Women had no
use for mosques at all, either socially or religiously; they
invariably prayed at home. Not a single woman interviewed even
mentioned them.

Despite the claims of some development agencies this discrepancy
between the needs and priorities of men and women raises some key
questions. Given the differences and restricted available
resources, which development project should be implemented first?
On what basis are decisions regarding project implementation
made? When local and international development agencies enter
the villages, who do they see and talk to? Men, or women, or

both? Whose project do they decide to implement? That of men, or
women? Admittedly, it may not be wise to divorce completely the
world of men from that of women, especially in the Palestinian
context, for the primary cause of underdevelopment at the village
level is structures and processes that exist in society at large.
But the effects of these are uneven, affecting men and women in
different ways, and leading to different priorities. This is not
intended to uphold the notion of intervention along exclusively
gender lines. But because of this problem, and because a clear-
cut division of labour separates the world of men from that of
women, the issue of differing priorities needs to be kept in mind
when planning and implementing village development projects.

Nevertheless, the position of women in these villages is
changing. Available evidence indicates that Palestinian women
have, over the years, increased their participation in all
spheres of life. The national question, improved educational
levels and the birth of separate women's organisations are some
of the factors that have contributed to an increased women's
consciousness and participation in political, economic and social
life. These factors have not only touched middle class city
dwellers, but have imparted their effects on rural women as well
(6). But the achievements, while at times remarkable, have been
far from satisfactory. In part, this is due to placing the
national contradiction in a primary position, to some extent at
the expense of the problems of gender as well as of social class.
Yet despite these problems, the manifestations of change are
evident and reflect themselves quite strongly in the differences
in the lifestyle and general consciousness between the older and
younger generations in these communities. One of the ways of
understanding these changes is to utilise anthropological
material to reconstruct the profiles of particular women in such
a way as to reflect the transformative effects on their lives
(7).

As the following stories will show, the economic and social
changes that have taken place over the years have had a dramatic
effect on women's lives. From lives that centre around the
domestic sphere - housework, for example, agricultural work on
family land, family labour or such highly skilled non-wage work
as midwifery or indigenous medicine - women have moved into the
public sphere into for example wage labour, education, and
general political activity. In between, women have lived the
dissolution of their family and domestic lives as a result of
outmigration and imprisonment. Women have begun to see their
lives differently; they aspire to more and have different
expectations.

The Changing World of Women

Sitti Sa'dieh (Grandmother Sa'dieh) was "the mother of the entire
village." She had delivered practically everyone, even the old
Mukhtar's children. She continued to do so for years, until
hospital delivery stormed the village. She was very old. Some

thought that she was over 100; others thought that she was probably around 80. No one really knew; but everyone agreed that she must have been an adult in the early twentieth century, when the Turks ruled the country. She told marvellously entertaining stories about those times; these stories were the ultimate testimony to her old age.

In many ways Sitti Sa'dieh was a relic of the past. Just like the land, she and the services she delivered to her community as a dayya (village midwife) have been marginalised over the years. By 1981, the combination of her old age and the village's changing childbirth patterns meant she had hardly any practice. By then, she was assisting deliveries only among the women of her family. It was during such an eventful occasion that we first met her. She was applying olive oil to the body of the newborn, kuhl (antinomy) to his eyes (8), and putting the final touches on his swaddle. It was a male, and therefore a time of great rejoicing. His mother had had three girls before him, and was threatened with divorce if she failed this time.

Sitti Sa'dieh was very suspicious of our presence. At first she hardly spoke to us, and flatly refused to perform her duties while we remained in the room. We, the team from the university, represented the "modern" world that had obliterated her past and shattered her present. She probably thought we were there to inspect and to report her to the public health authorities. After all, she was practising without a licence. She began to relax when she found out that we were advocates of breastfeeding, but it took a lengthy process of reassurance to establish a relationship of sufficient trust to allow her to unfold her past and present thoughts.

She came from a very poor background. Her mother had practised midwifery for many years before Sitti Sa'dieh took over what had become a family tradition. She had received much training from her mother, but never in the formal or modern ways. She practised because her skills were a gift from God, and because her services on earth would earn her a good life after death. She was very proud of having delivered most of the "men" of the village, even those who were abroad in the Gulf and earning quite a bit of money. Although she received presents - money or other things - from the families of the women she attended, she did not acknowledge her practice as work, but as a service to her community. It was reciprocity, not income, that mattered. Throughout her life she had been living in an extended family and did not completely rely on her practice to make a living. But she did earn a reasonable amount from her work and used it to supplement the family income. She was also a herbalist; and the combination of the two types of practice had meant financial security at some point in the past. She did not remember when, exactly, her practice took a downhill turn, but estimated it to be around the 1950s and 1960s. (This was a time when Jordanian state health and education services were being introduced at the village level.) But the downhill trend took a much sharper turn after the beginning of Israeli military occupation. By the late

1970s, modern medical facilities and drugs were rapidly sub-
stituting for her practice and her herbs.

Sitti Sa'dieh lamented the state of mind and stubbornness of the
younger generation of women of the village:

> They do not listen ... they think that just because
> they can read and write they know better about
> everything in this world. Not only do they deliver
> their children in town, but they also come back with
> the bottle, insisting that powdered milk is better for
> their child's health than breast milk.

She could not explain to us why she thought breast milk was
better for children than powdered milk in medical terms. Her
explanation, however, had a logic of its own:

> God gave women breasts and the milk that comes out of
> them for a purpose; and the purpose is not to throw the
> milk away and use something else instead.

To Sitti Sa'dieh, the modern-day village woman and her general
attitudes towards life were a mystery:

> They do not want to marry young, and want to go to
> school in the town instead. Yes, education of girls
> may be a good idea, but it also makes them arrogant.
> Besides "al-jizeh sutra" (marriage is a protection)
> (9).

Education was a substitute for marriage to Sitti Sa'dieh. And a
delayed age of marriage meant an increased risk of a swing
towards the immoral path that women could take as a result of the
unmarried and unprotected state. Even her own granddaughters had
resisted early marriage. But, thank God, they were now married
off, to their cousins.

The younger generation's attitude to traditional medical
practices was most saddening to Sitti Sa'dieh. Though some
still sought her help and the help of her competitor, the dayya
of the other hara (street or village subsection), no woman was
interested in or willing to learn her craft, not even her own
daughters and granddaughters. This meant that when she and her
competitor died, traditional medicine would cease to exist, at
least in its centralised and personalised form. Sitti Sa'dieh
took this to heart, for it symbolised the end of an era, her own.
It also symbolised the final and decisive break between the
tradition handed down over many years and the present-day
realities of life in the village.

We found Um-Salameh (the mother of Salameh) (10) by the taboun
(local traditional oven). She was trying to do two things at
once: bake her bread and gossip with the group of women who were
waiting for their turn to use the oven. Tabouns are shared by a
few households, usually related by blood or marriage, and to a

lesser extent by neighbours. There are many good reasons for sharing a <u>taboun</u>. To begin with, its capacity generally exceeds the average daily needs of one family. It is completely hand-made from a mixture of clay, hay, stones and other materials found in nature. But it requires a substantial amount of maintenance, and sharing reduces the workload. Sharing its fuel - a mixture of firewood, dried leaves, and animal manure - reduces the costs as well. Yet an unintended consequence of <u>taboun</u> sharing of importance to women is that baking bread is one of the few times when women can meet other women and socialise during the working day. While working on the land does provide an outlet for socialising, it is seasonal rather than daily and the nature of the work does not lend itself to the type of social sessions that occur by the <u>taboun</u>. Although many women visit each other's home during the late afternoons, some are denied these opportunities by their husbands, mothers-in-law or fathers. Baking the bread, like collecting water from the spring, provides these women with the necessary legitimacy for contact with others.

Um-Salameh's face was flushed from the heat of both the fire and the discussion. The topic was the <u>leshka</u> women (village women who were wage workers in Israel (11). According to Um-Salameh, the <u>leshka</u> women were mostly agricultural labourers:

> Along with children and, God forbid, with men, they leave their homes in the early morning hours before sunrise and, imagine, in the dark. They are transported into Israeli farms by way of a special Israeli truck [intended to facilitate the transport of workers from the territories' villages to Israel]. They return, once again, in the dark and in the company of men. They return carrying vegetables and fruits that have been obtained from the farms where they work, and feed them to their families.

All of the women labourers of the region, according to the women at the <u>taboun</u>, came from refugee camps. The women categorically denied that women from the village or from nearby villages worked in Israel. They insisted that this phenomenon was restricted to refugee camps, that village people would never allow such a thing to happen to their women and daughters. Um-Salameh summed up the collective position regarding women and wage labour by saying, '<u>ihna ma 'ndnash niswan bitishtghel</u>' ('We do not have women who work.')

Apparently, a significant amount of stigma was attached to wage labour among women, especially if they sought work in Israel. The reasons were in part spelled out by one of the participants in the discussion:

> The <u>leshka</u> women behave in a loose and immoral way. Going away from the village to work means meeting strange men, and having to deal with them and to keep their company. It also means coming back home in the

dark, unaccompanied ... All these excessive liberties
are bound to make a weak woman go astray ... I tell
you, they end up behaving in a very immoral way. Look
at what happened when one of the leshka women from the
nearby refugee camp came to visit our village. She was
standing in the street, talking with other women. A
young and handsome donkey rider was passing by. She
must have fancied him. So she ran towards him and
jumped on the back of the donkey and circled her arms
around the rider's waist. Do you call that moral
behaviour?

But there is at least one reason for the stigma attached to
women's wage labour, which was not spelled out by the participants. In Palestinian culture, women and children, the
"weaker" sector of society, are seen as the responsibility of
men. The obligations of men towards women are varied; but one
important obligation is to provide an adequate income. This
holds true even in peasant villages that rely on agriculture as a
primary source of income, where women participate to a considerable extent in working the land. Despite women's work on
the farm, the financial aspects of the operation and the ultimate
responsibility for the family's income are the men's domain.
When a woman leaves her house or village in search of paid work,
it is seen as an indication that the male household members can
no longer provide sufficient income to fulfil their family's
needs. Otherwise, why would the men allow the women to work? To
the villagers, this is a source of shame, not only to the woman's
husband and in-laws, but also to her parents.

Um-Salameh's confidence, eloquence and general attitude towards
other women and ourselves reflected her economic and social
position in the village. She was the wife, and the only wife, of
one of the two village Mukhtars. She came from a well-to-do
background and married into a landed and notable family. All her
male children were abroad, working in the Gulf. She boasted that
they were all educated and held important technical positions.
One of her sons had just left the village the year before. He
went to work with his brothers, leaving his young wife and two
sons under her care. Um-Salameh's house was full of the evidence
of remittance money: spaciousness, electrical gadgets, even a
private internal piped water supply connected to an electric
pump. The evidence of remittance: the motor of the water supply;
the refrigerator, the colour television; the cassette player,
were arranged for display, as status symbols as well as for use.
Pictures of the migrants were hung everywhere, as stark reminders
of the price in separation families must pay for this newly
generated wealth.

Yet, despite all this, Um-Salameh was mother earth herself. She
insisted on tilling the land herself and showed us some of the
family land she tilled. What she grew was used for family
consumption, not for sale. No, she said, they did not need that
source of food, but the land had to be tilled to keep the
tradition alive. She took over the tilling because the family

land was being neglected. The children were away and the father was too old to work it himself or oversee the work of paid labourers. Even their olive trees were being neglected, and this was a source of deep concern for her. She seemed of two minds over the issue of migration. On the one hand, she approved of it because of all the new opportunities it brought to her family. Despite the separation, the bond between the family members was not weakened by their departure, she believed, but strengthened, especially among the brothers. On the other hand, the increasing difficulties that she and her husband faced in tilling the land, and its neglect as a result of her sons' departure, was becoming an almost unbearable thought. Unlike <u>Sitti</u> Sa'dieh, Um-Salameh was caught between two worlds, with different values. She consoled herself with the thought that, after all, it would have been very difficult for all of her sons to make a good living had they stayed in the village. She also consoled herself with the idea that at least her sons were working in Arab countries and in respectable non-manual jobs, unlike many other men from the nearby village, who were well-educated but forced by circumstances to work in Israel as wage labourers. In the end, it appeared as if she was accepting the present and parting with the past.

Um-'Odeh (the mother of 'Odeh) was about 45 years old. She had grown up in the town, but had been living in the village for 20 years, ever since she married 'the most respectable and the most educated man in the village'. Her husband was an office worker somewhere in Jerusalem; and was reputed to be a wise man, and the source of many village collective initiatives. Um-'Odeh was a well-educated woman, having completed her secondary schooling. She appeared to be well integrated into village life, although with time we learned that she was not exactly comfortable with it. She managed the affairs of the household with a slight, but deliberate, difference. She wore spectacles, something of a rarity in the village, and Western dresses instead of the traditional embroidered dresses the majority of women used for daily clothing. In this, she even surpassed some of the younger women, who wore Western skirts but put trousers underneath for modesty. She and other village women who had lived abroad were the only ones who kept bins with plastic rubbish bags inside their homes.

Um-'Odeh's presentation of herself to others, but especially to those of us from town, was interesting. As soon as she knew of our presence and intentions ('filling questionnaires', as she put it), she made sure we understood certain facts about herself: that she was highly educated and therefore enlightened; that she understood quite well why we were in the village and therefore could help us; and that she greatly desired to help her community. Um-'Odeh was already active in a range of projects. She had been hired by Birzeit University's literacy programme and found to be intelligent, 'the best teacher around'. Since she had received basic first aid training in high school (something no other village woman could boast of) she took it upon herself to set up a first aid station in the village and had saved lives.

She had rented out a room in her house to Birzeit University's literacy programme and was also earning money from "respectable" office work. She thus became our informant, and confidante, and eventually proved instrumental in mobilising the village women around a health care project.

Yet, despite all of this, it was clear that Um-'Odeh still felt ambivalent about her marriage. On the one hand, it was a streak of luck that she had married at all. She had been in her late twenties and a <u>baira</u> (leftover) when he proposed. On the other hand, he was not a fantastic "catch": much older than she was, previously married, with five other children and, most important- ly, a villager. Rather than face the life of an old maid, Um- 'Odeh had chosen a downwardly mobile marriage. When we met her, many years later, she seemed to be still assessing the results of that choice.

We had known Um-Ahmad (the mother of Ahmad) for almost a year before the survey. She was a patient in the clinic the Charita- ble Society and Birzeit University operated. She was pregnant then, and seriously anaemic and underweight. Yet for months she was neither willing to talk, help herself, or even accept a home visit by <u>Sit</u> Faouzieh, our field nurse. Eventually, the extra attention and care that <u>Sit</u> Faouzieh afforded to her made her open up, even break down and cry, and tell us her story. She had been married for about 12 years when her wage-labourer husband was suddenly arrested by the Israeli army. She had not seen him since; he remained in prison for a 'security' offence, without a formal charge sheet or trial. Having lost the protection of her imprisoned husband, Um-Ahmad had fallen under the direct thumb of her mother-in-law, whom she had never liked. Her mother-in-law had been hiding food away from her in locked cupboards, making it practically impossible for her to eat properly. <u>Sit</u> Faouzieh talked to the mother-in-law about the effect of good nutrition on the development of babies, especially male babies, and the pregnancy was completed uneventfully, though the newborn child was slightly underweight.

Um-Ahmad was not at home when we went to visit her. She was fetching water for her family from the village spring, about three kilometres from her house. We followed her, hoping to join her and her water collection circle in conversation. We were not disappointed; a small group of women, some children, and a few donkeys were all gathered by the spring, and the discussion was ongoing.

She was very happy to see us and to introduce us to her friends. Um-Sami was a woman in her thirties whose husband was also in prison, but under very different conditions. Just a few months after their marriage, her husband had left the village to seek work in Germany. For a while, he sent money back to his family and all seemed to be going well. One day, however, the money and the letters stopped; it took several months for Um-Sami to discover that her husband was serving a seven-year prison sentence in a German prison. Although she had no idea whatsoever

about what had happened, she kept swearing to his complete
innocence. His imprisonment left her and her child completely
dependent on the charity of his relatives and a few of the kinder
village souls. Theresa was Columbian, and was married to a
village member who had migrated to Latin America in the 1950s for
work. One day he had decided to make the return home a reality,
and had brought back his family, including the gharibeh or
ajnabieh (stranger or foreigner), along with some savings which
he used to start up a chicken farm in the village. He soon
became bored with village life, and returned to Columbia, this
time alone. That was the last Theresa saw or heard from him.
Rumour had it that he was married again to another Columbian
woman. Theresa, despite the problems of language, and other
severe hardships, still managed to make a living for herself and
her children by working as a maid in the town.

Life was becoming even more difficult for Um-Ahmad. Her husband
was still in prison, and her mother-in-law, although slightly
tamer, had basically not changed her taghieh (tyrannical)
behaviour. It was now increasingly difficult to make ends meet,
with hyperinflation in food prices, and given that she and her
family did not own cultivable land (this was very unusual). To
Um-Ahmad, it was as if all the catastrophes occurred together,
to spite, or even to break her. Just a few months before, the
household water cistern had broken down; the money needed for
major repairs was simply not available. Since then, Um-Ahmad had
to collect all the family's water from the spring. She estimated
that it required about four to five hours of her time every other
day to supply the family with the water absolutely necessary for
survival. The water containers had to be carried on her head and
uphill, all the way to her house. 'Lucky is the woman who has a
donkey,' she lamented. Her 10-year-old daughter did help
sometimes, but helping meant the girl was being distracted from
her studies. It already seemed that the girl was failing her
class that year, which worried Um-Ahmad. But there was little
that she could do, and she was contemplating pulling the girl
completely out of school if this state of affairs continued. She
could not even begin to confront the problem of the late summer
months and autumn, when the spring would dry up and they would be
forced to purchase water from a vendor in town.

The village elders had made several attempts to solve the water
problem. Although the money was available to install a piped
water supply, the stumbling block was the acquisition of a permit
from the Israeli military authorities. Acquiring this permit
seemed to involve waiting forever. The villagers were not even
allowed control over their own village spring water. When some
of the village leaders and others attempted to obtain a permit
from the military authorities to connect the spring - through
pipes and a pump - to an outlet in the village that is more
accessible to the women, the response was negative. They were
told that

the spring water, even the rain water, are the property
of the State of Israel.

Salma was just 20 years old and had been refusing marriage with a remarkable degree of strength. Her father worked as a construction worker in Israel. An Israeli workers' bus transported him and others from his village and other nearby villages to their workplace, 'deep in the heart of enemy territory'. They worked and slept there, both illegally, throughout the week and came home on the Sabbath, the Israeli day of rest from work. Salma's father's children hardly saw him, for their rest from school was Friday. He had been working in Israel for some ten years. At first he worked intensively, and was hardly ever unemployed. But then he fell from a height at the construction site where he worked and injured his back. He could not collect any of the health or social security benefits that an Israeli worker would have collected in the same situation; for he was a Palestinian Arab, and worked in Israel illegally. For months he was incapacitated, during which the family underwent terrible hardships. Eventually, although he did not completely recover, he went back to work in Israel, under the strain of a steadily deteriorating back.

Although Salma thoroughly rejected her father's attitudes towards life and was deeply pained by the way he treated her, she nevertheless succeeded in rising above her own reality enough to retain a strong sympathy towards him and his lot in life. She had been at odds with her father for quite some time. The problem between them was the marriage/education dichotomy. He wanted to marry her off as soon as possible; and she wanted education. Her great ambition in life was to earn a university degree. Her dream was not altogether unrealistic; some of her friends in the nearby village had already made it to university. One of them was writing poetry for publication; another had gone to the Soviet Union to earn a professional degree; a third was at Birzeit University, heavily involved in nationalist and resistance activities, in addition to learning. They had been all at high school together when Salma's father decided to keep her at home during her last year of high school. Although she was at home, Salma did not give up. She secretly registered for the high school exam and studied for it alone, at home, after the family went to sleep. But the duress of the situation did not allow her to succeed. When we met her she was preparing for another attempt. Despite all this, and despite her own exasperation, she did not resent her father, but tried to work around his limitations. She understood the constraints of illiteracy, poverty, the lack of exposure, and all the work and social pressures her father's ideas were shaped by. Nevertheless, she was adamant at changing them: 'One day he will learn how to respect me,' she kept saying. Salma was unbreakable.

Salma was a woman of deep conflict. Her relationship to her family and her village was one of love and hate. She could not deny her attachment to her village and its people; but she abhorred the old mentality and its repercussions on the lives of women. Although she felt victimised by her village origins, she could not stop thinking about new initiatives for village improvement. Her main outlet was books. Her house was relatively full of them: Lenin, Engels, Nawal al-Sa'dawi (an Egyptian feminist), Ghassan Kanafani (a Palestinian writer and martyr) and many others. Books were her salvation. They were the cracks in this house of darkness, which kept her in touch with outside worlds, and alive. To her father, however, books were the origin of his daughter's strange and utterly unacceptable way of thinking; he hated them with a passion. Yet he could not bring himself to deny her those as well, for he loved her. He felt a terrible sense of guilt about making her leave school. But what could he do? He could not afford to pay her way through high school along with her brothers, so he opted to educate his male children instead. Besides, the social pressure on him was becoming unbearable:

> What do you want me to do? Last year, she was coming back from school very late. She had to walk from Birzeit and alone, sometimes even in the dark. She used to attend these meetings where men were present. That is why she was so frequently late. And they used to read those damn books, the cause of all troubles. It was those people who gave her the books that instigated her against me and her family. They flipped her brain upside down ... I was no longer able to walk in the streets of the village with my head up. Everyone was gossiping about Salma and her behaviour. There was only one thing for me to do, and that was to keep her at home, away from school and those book people.

Salma's strong sense of nationalism was the source of additional conflict. At a time when she and the "book people" were preaching and instigating against having any dealings whatsoever with the Israeli enemy, her father, right under her nose, was providing her and her family with daily bread by working for the enemy in "yet to be liberated territories". The conflict reached an unprecedented level when her father broke a leadership call for a strike of Palestinian workers in Israel. Salma was traumatised by the event, to a point that forced her to rethink her political principles. It was then that she began the process of understanding the complexity of the problem. It was then, too, that she began to see her father as a victim of aggression and colonialism rather than as a traitor. She paid for this new understanding, however, by her partial alienation from her group; they thought her new position was deviationist and possibly dangerous.

Eventually, Salma's relationship with her group mended, and was even solidified. The experience the movement was gaining brought a maturity that allowed for increasingly complex and sophisticated analysis to emerge. This reflected itself organisationally in many positive ways. One of them was the emergence of a women's national movement separate from, but still tied to, that of men. A separate, national, but also feminist movement solved the problems many Palestinian women faced in attempting to join the men in the national liberation struggle. This became Salma's other outlet: By the end of 1981, a women's committee had been established next door to her house.   Today, four years later, Salma is a second-year university student.

NOTES

1. The same saying was used in Hilma Graquist's Artas of the 1920s.   See Grandquist, H, <u>Marriage Conditions in a Palestinian Village</u>, Vol III, Helsingfore, 1935, p. 166.

2. For a description of how the institutions of family and religion define the role and status of Palestinian women, see Haddad, Y, 'Problems of Legitimation and Domination', in Nakleh & Zureik, op cit, pp. 147-75.

3. This law that governs inheritance as well as others that legitimise the subordination of women are derived from Islamic <u>Sharia</u> laws.   For further information see, for instance, Tabari, A & Yegemeh, N, <u>In the Shadow of Islam: The Women's Movement in Iran</u>, Zed Press, London, 1982, p. 12.

4. A tendency of women to renounce their inheritance in favour of their brothers so as to maintain property in an unfragmented state is not uncommon.   See Haddad, in Nakleh & Zureik, op cit, p. 149.

5. On the issue of reduced wages of Palestinian workers in Israel in comparison to Israeli workers, see, for instance, Benvenisti, op cit; Farjoun, in Rothschild, op cit.   See also Artzieli, M, 'The Arabs Cause Inflation and Unemployment', <u>Ha'aretz</u>, 16.11.81 and in <u>Israel Mirror</u> no 718, 31.1.85.

6. See Sayigh, R, 'Encounters with Palestinian Women under Occupation', <u>Journal of Palestine Studies</u>, Vol 10, no 4, 1981, pp. 3-26; Haddad, in Nakhleh, op cit; Giacaman, R, 'Palestinian Women and Development', op cit.

7. To present a clearer and more descriptive picture of social change, the profiles of seven women were incorporated into the characterisation of five.

8. <u>Kuhl</u> is a locally made preparation of pulverised antimony that is applied to the eyelids of women for aesthetic reasons, and the eyelids of newborns for the prevention of eye infection.   In the Western scientific tradition it is common for silver nitrate solution to be applied to the conjunctiva of newborns for the prevention of neonatal conjunctivitis.   Thus the principle for the application of both compounds is similar, even though the therapeutic use of <u>Kuhl</u> has not been established.

9. For a very interesting account of marriage conditions in a Palestinian village in the 1920s, see Granquist, H, <u>Marriage Conditions in a Palestinian Village</u>, Helsingfors, 1931.

10. Among Palestinians, parenthood is an important status and is reflected in the way parents are addressed. Once a male child is born the parents are called after the name of the child, with <u>Abu</u> preceding the child's name in the case of fathers and <u>Um</u> in the case of mothers. In the event where no children are born to couples, the name of the husband's father is used to address the couple, as if to disguise the lack of parenthood and therefore status. In cases where only female children are born, the father's father's name is used for the purpose. Alternatively, the name of the first-born female child is used, but on rare occasions.

11. <u>Leshka</u> is a Hebrew word that has been adapted into Arabic among some Palestinian communities; it denotes the hiring by the Israeli Bureau of Employment in Israel of Palestinian Arab workers from the occupied territories.

A view of one of the villages

The village store, full of highly processed foods,
the symbols of modern living

Construction workers building village homes during their
Sabbath from work in Israel

Children, especially male children, are highly regarded in
these communities. They ultimately substitute the functions
of a Welfare State

The village <u>dayya</u> ...

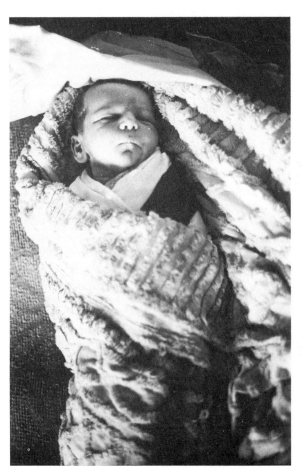

... and the child she delivered.
Note the swaddle.

Washing dishes and clothes. Housework usually takes place
in the courtyard for most of the year.

Collecting water from the village spring - sometimes walk
3 to 4 kilometres carrying water

A <u>taboun</u> gossip session ... one of the few opportunities
for women to meet outside the home

In the late afternoon leisure hours, when all the housework is completed, the women embroider

She insisted that her granddaughters visiting from the Gulf should learn the old craft

CHAPTER FIVE

FERTILITY AND MORTALITY

Fertility Data

In these villages, the reproductive life cycle had shifted. Gone were the days of child marriage and <u>atiet el-jorah</u> (formula for betrothal at birth) (1). Women's age at first marriage had clearly risen; women between the ages of 15 and 29 had a mean first marriage age of 19.1 compared to 17.6 for women aged 30 to 49. The mean first marriage age for the total married women of childbearing age was 18.8 years. There were 272 of them, or 43 per cent of the female population over 15 years old. The rest were older women (26 per cent), students (13 per cent, or 50 per cent of the 15-19 age group) or women who were waiting for their <u>nasib</u> (luck; i.e., a husband), for <u>ibn-al-halal</u> (the unforbidden man, the right man) (Table 5.1).

TABLE 5.1

WOMEN OVER THE AGE OF 15 YEARS BY STATUS

Status	Number	Percentage of total
Married and between the ages of 15-49	272	43
Fifty years old and over	164	26
Students	80	13
Other and unmarried	115	18
Total	631	

Of those married and 15-49 years old, a solid 79 per cent had children under three years old. The rest either had no children in this age category, or none at all (Table 5.2).

TABLE 5.2

MARRIED WOMEN OF CHILDBEARING AGE (15-49 YEARS)
BY THE PRESENCE OF CHILDREN

Number of children by mother	Total Number	Percentage of total
One child under 3	159	58
Two children under 3	53	20
Three children under 3	5	2
Children only over the age of 3	35	13
No children at all	20	7
Total	272	100

Despite the rising age at first marriage, fertility was high in these communities. An estimation of fertility among all the currently married women yielded the figure of 8.67 for total fertility and 43/1000 for the crude birth rate (2) (Appendix 4). These figures were substantially higher than those obtained for Egypt in 1976, with a total fertility of 5.16 and a crude birth rate of 35/1000 (3). They were, however, almost identical to the figures for the West Bank population as a whole, where the birth rate for 1981 was 44.3/1000 (4), and where vital registration data indicated that fertility was rising, at least up to 1979 (5). The estimated birth rate for the three communities, as well as for Palestinians living in the West Bank and Gaza, however, appears the same as the birth rates for Palestinian refugees living in Jordan and Syria (6).

Until the mid-1960s, early marriage provided a substantial number of advantages to a peasant household. Within the framework of the extended family, women's labour was needed in the home. This encouraged mothers to request the sons' marriage. Moreover, as Hilma Grandquist noted, both the logic of adaptation and moral arguments encouraged young marriage:

> The young girl gradually grows into the customs and views of her husband's family; one need not fear that she will come in with her own ideas and wishes if she has in her early years lived under the disciplining hand of her mother-in-law, who has moulded her according to her own desire (7).

And,

> Moral reasons are in favour of early marriage ... early marriage is considered extremely desirable for girls seeing that an unmarried woman is very much exposed to moral danger (8).

Moral, logistic, and material reasons for early marriage meant people considered that the earlier a girl was married off the better; otherwise, the price was high for everyone. A 25-year-old bride, for example, was considered something doubtful (9). By 1981, these moral, logistic, and material bases for early marriage had been, in our three villages, if not eroded, modified substantially. As has been stated, almost three-quarters of the households were occupied by nuclear families, which reduced the need for women's labour in the home. Modern devices, which also reduced labour, freed women to some extent to participate in other activities, such as education. Especially after 1967, the possibilities of obtaining work in Israel and abroad meant an increase in the ability of young couples to establish a household separately from the extended family. It also translated into a general improvement in living conditions at the household level, as expressed by the presence of amenities of various sorts. Thus, mother-in-laws no longer required the additional labour of the young bride; for their own households now are not only supported by mechanical instead of manual labour, but are smaller in size. These changes, coupled with an increased educational level, especially among women, and a generally changing outlook, have had their impact on the moral code. A 25-year-old bride is no longer a source of suspicion. One must not exaggerate these modifications of the moral code, however. Even in the towns, an unmarried woman in her early thirties is still considered <u>baira</u> (left over, on the shelf, that is, not worthy of marriage), if not a doubtful phenomenon.

What is needed now is an explanation of the persistence of high fertility despite the reduced time span when women are able to biologically reproduce. Here, Claude Meillassoux's thesis on the economic bases of demographic reproduction may be of some use (10). According to this thesis, demographic reproduction is conditioned by the mode of production in specific communities. In what he calls the 'domestic mode of production' where families primarily depend on subsistence agriculture, the birth rate is relatively lower than in other modes. Progressive integration of communities into the market economy, wage-earning and the loss of control over grain reserves, however, change the conditions of demographic reproduction. Demographic reproduction becomes dependent on money income, prices of subsistence and levels of employment, among other factors. These circumstances and the ensuing insecurity favour both a higher birth rate as a means of social security, and an increased lifespan for the younger generations. They also make more prominent the effects of famine and unemployment.

In the Palestinian context, land marginalisation and integration into the market economy and wage-earning have been occurring for many years, since at least the turn of the century (11). These processes have been sharply accentuated, however, by the Arab-Israeli War of 1948; the resultant dispossession and dispersion of a substantial proportion of the population; and by the conditions and consequences of military occupation, as shown earlier for the three villages. Work in Israel and abroad, and the increasing marginalisation of land did mean an increasing dependence on children - on their labour and, through educating them, on their increased earning power - as a form of security for those who have not been dispossessed altogether. For refugees, wage labour and security in the form of children became the only means of survival. Coupled with the haunting shadow of Israeli land confiscation, these factors make the high Palestinian birth rate quite understandable. But the politics of dispossession and dispersion are also important because of their effects on the collective and individual consciousness. Palestinians have responded to aggression in various ways, and one of these ways is resistance by means of what is called the "demographic factor". The higher the birth rate, the larger the number of Palestinians, and the better future ability to conquer the aggressor, the logic goes. It is as if the loss of Palestine as a geo-political entity has caused Palestinians to cling to their national, cultural, and political identities, and reinforce them in all ways possible, including demographically.

In the context of the three villages, although wage relations did develop at the expense of kinship relations - as is exemplified by the apparent trend towards nuclear families for instance - the latter persist as a means of security, though in a somewhat modified form. They persist primarily because work opportunities in Israel and abroad remained unstable and, as Meillassoux suggested, they therefore continued to be a basis for security, albeit not the sole one. The conditions of wage labour in Israel or abroad, then, have had contradictory effects in these communities. On the one hand, wage labour provided the means through which children could be freed from economic and social control by their parents. On the other, job insecurity meant the necessity of maintaining kinship ties. The net effect could be seen as favouring a high birth rate. The new forms of kinship relations appear to be beneficial for both parents and children. From the children's point of view, wage labour provides the means to achieve at least partial control over their lives. For the parents, domestic agricultural productivity is no longer a major source of wealth. Wage labour in Israel and remittances from abroad as new sources of wealth encourage parents to have children, not only in order to reap immediate benefits, but as a security for old age as well.

Infant and Child Mortality

If one were to predict future fertility trends based on the above, one would expect the fertility rate in these communities to remain relatively high and unchanged, as long as the prevailing political and economic relationships continue. But the fertility picture is also influenced by infant and child mortality patterns, which there is reason to believe are on a decline. The birth histories of the 272 married women of childbearing age revealed 1578 births in total: 821 males and 757 females (Table 5.3). This means a sex ratio of 1.085 (M/F), which is slightly higher than the generally expected 1.05 (12) at birth. This variation between the expected and the actual ratios could be entirely due to chance, given the small population under consideration. It could also be due to incomplete reporting of

female births and deaths.   A third possible explanation is an
altered sex ratio at birth in this population.   This phenomenon,
though unusual, has been known to occur (13).   Because there is
no clear way to distinguish which of these factors was causative
in this case, the discrepancy cannot be fully comprehended.   What
can be said, keeping in mind the possibility of underreporting of
female births and deaths, is that mortality estimates generated
from this data represent the minimum level of mortality this
population has experienced.

TABLE 5.3

BIRTHS, DEATHS AND INFANT AND CHILD MORTALITY RATES
BY SEX

	Male	Female	Total
Total born	821	757	1578
Total dead	150	146	295
Proportion dead	0.193	0.182	0.187
Total women			272
Mean births/woman			5.79
Mean deaths/woman			1.085
Sex ratio at birth			1.085
Mean infant mortality rate	90	91	
Mean mortality under 2 years	108	113	
Mean mortality	115	124	

The proportions indicated in Table 5.3 yield higher childhood
mortality estimates for girls than for boys (14) (also Appendix
5).   Although the small size of the sample does not allow for
conclusive statements, and introduces the possibility of chance
variations, they may be of significance considering that male
age-specific death rates are generally higher than female rates.
There are exceptions that appear to be limited to certain age
groups, mostly ages in early childhood and during the female
reproductive period (15).   These exceptions occur in other Third
World countries (16) and appear to be associated with a low
living standard (17) and with environmental disadvantages for
females (18).   Underenumeration of female births and deaths
cannot be completely ruled out as a cause for this variation, nor
can the effects of chance.   But in some Third World countries,
underenumeration could not account solely or even substantially
for the observed abnormally high sex ratio (M/F) (19) among the
wider population.   Males are usually inherently more vulnerable
to infant mortality than females.   Although the causes of this
vulnerability are not yet completely understood, it appears that
X-linked immunoregulatory genes contribute to greater female
resistance to infectious diseases (20) which, in turn, may
positively influence the chance of survival of females during
infancy.   Despite this biological disadvantage for males, females
have been known to have higher mortality and higher specifically
infectious disease mortality than males in certain situations.
This suggests that environmental and socio-cultural factors are
the cause.

Given the constraints of the data available for the three
villages, conclusive statements simply cannot be made on this
question. What can be pointed to, however, is the preferential
treatment of male children as a possible cause for the differential in mortality. If we combine the statistical parameters
relating to childhood deaths with morbidity patterns, as well as
other behavioural and non-quantifiable parameters, we can
actually make stronger statements. Though morbidity and other
data will be elaborated in detail later, some of it is useful
here. It was found, for instance, that the overall rate of
malnutrition among female children under 3 years old in these
villages was almost double that of males in the same age group.
Within this age category, females were consistently more
malnourished than males at all ages. The severity of malnutrition among the females was greater as well, with 20 per cent of
the females being moderately malnourished, in contrast to only 7
per cent for the males. While feeding and weaning data showed
some differential treatment patterns by mothers - in favour of
male children - that cannot be considered statistically significant, the ethnographic material collected as well as a work
relationship of four years with many of the women in these
communities does indicate that male children tended to be given
better and more food. The reduction in the rate of malnutrition
with increasing education of mothers was sharper for males than
for females. Male children tended to be taken to health care
facilities more often and earlier, and their health status
observed more closely by mothers. In all, male children were
better cared for and more highly regarded by both parents.

While the issue of preferential treatment of male children and
its impact on childhood survival cannot be settled here, it does
raise some key questions. If, as the mortality and morbidity
data suggest, gender is indeed a determinant of health status
and survival, then what are its implications for intervention
programmes? How can this problem be approached so that it can be
taken into account by policymakers, planners and activists? And,
most importantly, within what context does this preferential
treatment occur and how can it be changed? Although this
question will be dealt with at a later stage, one thing is clear
here: change in these patterns requires social action at more
than one level and cannot be accomplished by medicine alone.

TABLE 5.4

CHILDHOOD AND INFANT MORTALITY ESTIMATES FOR BOTH SEXES
BASED ON THE BRASS METHOD/TRUSSEL VERSION/WEST MODEL

Marriage duration in years	Reference period t_x in years	Mortality rate per 1000 live births		
		infant under 1 year of age	childhood under 2	under 3
0-4	1.37	94	115	124
5-9	3.5	68	80	86
10-14	5.7	111	137	149
Mean	3.5 (1972)	91	111	120

Estimates of mortality in infancy and childhood for both sexes based on data on cohorts of women classified by duration of marriage and on children ever born yielded mean mortality for infants and for children under the ages of 2 and 3 years of 91, 111 and 120 deaths per 1000 live births respectively (Table 5.4 and Appendix 5). These figures refer to a time period (t_x) about three to four years before the survey, that is, around 1977-78. Table 5.4 shows that infant and childhood deaths are higher among the 0-4 and 10-14-year marriage duration groups than the 5-9 one. This J-shaped pattern is apparently common in the Middle East as well as other areas (22), and can be explained in various ways. One possibility is that the higher-than-expected death rates obtained for the 0-4-year marriage duration groups are due to the overrepresentation of first-born children in this group. First-born are known to have a higher risk of death than second and higher order children. A second possible explanation is that child mortality has been declining over time. Other than for the 0-4 years' marriage duration, an increase in the proportion of dead children can be observed for all other groups with increasing duration of marriage (Appendix 5) and appears to support the view that childhood mortality has been declining.

The small number of women in each duration group, however, does mean that the observed differences could be due to chance. Because of this, the most reliable step to take is to average the mortality rates for the three groups; this increases the sample size threefold and reduces chance variations to an acceptable level. Although averaging means that the ability to conclusively delineate time trends is lost, the observed trends strongly suggest a pattern of decreasing infant and childhood mortality throughout the 1970s. The average infant mortality rate of 91 deaths/1000 live births obtained for these villages, moreover, were found to be close to the rate of 82/1000 obtained for the West Bank for the same year (23), but lagged behind the rate of 70/1000 for Jordan during the 1972-76 period (24).

If infant mortality is taken as the principal proxy measure of health, then health in these communities appears to be improving. The underlying assumption here is that causes of mortality are similar to the major causes of morbidity (25), and that infant deaths are good indicators of the state of economic and social development and health in particular communities, since they tend to be good measures of the effects of nutrition, public health, income and general environment on health (26). In the absence of other material that would delineate health trends for the past 20 years or so in these communities, infant mortality becomes the only available evidence for the state of health. But it must be approached with caution. Infant mortality and the mortality rate in general fails to specify the causes of deaths. They also fail to indicate whether the causes of mortality have been changing or not. In societies undergoing rapid change, causes of death and morbidity could also be changing, and influencing the health picture in a manner that cannot be elaborated by an examination of death rates alone. Further, infant mortality rates do not specify the quality of life of those who survive. Although they

may be less likely to die, they may also be likely to be
unhealthy due to diseases that were endemic at an earlier stage.
They may also be unhealthy due to new diseases which may not take
their toll in deaths, but in morbidity instead.

The trend towards improvement in mortality levels suggested for
these communities does not differ from the overall trend for
Third World or underdeveloped countries. A reduction in
mortality at all ages has been noted for these countries over the
past two decades (27). Moreover, the same improvement trend for
infant mortality has been recorded for other Arab countries, such
as Jordan (28).

Mortality risk, especially in early childhood, has been associated with a variety of biological and socio-economic
indicators. Nutritional status in early childhood; diarrhoeal
and other infections; other preventable diseases; low birth
weight; high fertility; mother's age; water and sanitation;
literacy and educational level; access to health care facilities;
and poverty are factors which have been identified as contributing to an increased risk of death (29). Although there have been
some attempts to elaborate the mechanisms through which the
various factors associated with mortality risk impart their
effects, they remain inadequate. There is little agreement on
how health determinants operate, and on the weight of each,
relative to others.

The impact of education on health, mortality, and rural development is a case in point (30). Although many agree that increased
education in general has a positive impact on health, and
therefore a reduced risk of death, there appears to be little
agreement on the mechanism involved. Definitional ambiguities
complicate the problem further. For example, one is generally
unable to understand the meaning of the term literacy status.
Does it mean the ability to read and write, and if so, what kind
of script? Or does it mean school attendance of any sort, and if
so, is this literacy status a functional one or not? How is the
decision on literacy status made: through the respondents'
answers or through testing the respondents' ability to read and
write? What compounds the problem even further is emerging
evidence that the impact of education on health behaviour, which
in turn influences mortality risk, can at times be negative. The
case of bottle-feeding is an important example of this contradictory effect of education on health (31). Although the net effect
of education on health and mortality risk may be positive, it
also, under certain conditions, can be negative. Although the
debate on mortality risks and their determinants is clearly
unresolved, it does highlight the need to take into consideration
biological and socio-economic determinants when examining
specific mortality trends. It also underlines the need for
research approaches compatible with difficult-to-quantify
parameters, such as feeding behaviour.

For the three villages, cross-tabulations of the proportions of
children dead for the 246 women who have had children with a

range of variables revealed some interesting results. A strong, positive correlation was found between the proportion of children dead and the age, literacy status and educational level of the mother (Tables 5.5 and 5.6). A similar association was found between the proportions of children dead and the miscarriage rate of mothers. Women who were 30 years or older had a higher proportion of their children dead than those under the age of 30. Given that the educational levels of mothers were increasing with decreasing age, the effects of age on the proportion of children dead reflects, in part, the higher educational level of younger mothers. But education is not the sole factor here; changing times, higher expectations, and increasing exposure to "modern ways" could play an important factor in determining health behaviour and, therefore, the risk of death.

TABLE 5.5

PROPORTION OF CHILDREN DEAD BY AGE OF MOTHER

Age of mother	No. of deaths	Proportion of children dead - %age of age group		total no of women
		1-20%	more than 20%	
15-19	100%	0	0	7
20-29	70%	7	23	74
30-39	38%	26	36	81
40-49	35%	19	46	80
Total				242

TABLE 5.6

PROPORTION OF CHILDREN DEAD BY EDUCATION OF MOTHER

Education of mother in years	Proportion of children dead - %age of education group			total women
	No deaths	1-20%	more than 20%	
0	38%	19	43	147
1-5	61%	17	22	46
6 or more	70%	10	20	50
Total				243

Chi Square 19.48   p = 0.001

Although we obtained information pertaining to reading and writing ability from respondents, it was not included in the analysis. On more than one occasion the response did not match the actual ability of the respondent to read standard Arabic script, for instance, a newspaper. Thus the responses to this question were deemed unreliable, and we included only the responses to questions relating to the total number of years of schooling. The years of schooling data was particularly interesting in its effect on deaths and health levels as well. What appeared to matter was not so much the first years of

schooling, but a critical point of four to five years. Death and
health levels within the family seemed to improve with increasing
education of the mother, but only if she had completed the fourth
or fifth year of schooling. Completing six or more years of
schooling, in the case of deaths among children, meant an
additional improvement. But this was not as sharp as the
difference between those who did not have any schooling and those
who had completed up to the fifth grade.

There was no significant association between the proportion of
children dead and the availability of household facilities
presumed important for health (refrigerator, piped water, and
latrines). Nor was there a significant association between the
proportions of children dead and such economic status indicators
as dependency ratio, crowding, the number of migrants in each
household and general wealth level (the average of the scores
obtained from the four informants). This was not unexpected,
since these parameters were probably changing over the years.
Their effects on childhood mortality, if any, had been taking
place for 20 years or 30 years in some cases, and could not be
measured based on their presence or absence at a much later date.
The only way to make sense out of a correlation between economic
status and death rate is to control for time. Because in this
case the sample size was too small to yield meaningful results,
such a correlation was not possible.

An explanation for the suggested improvement in childhood
mortality level during the 1970s can be sought by looking at the
communities' changing living conditions. As stated earlier, the
trend towards a reduction in mortality has been observed for the
Palestinian population for at least the past 30 years. This
trend has, by and large, followed the progressive improvement in
general living conditions taking place in the area. State
schooling and health services began to reach villages in the
1950s. This trend continued during the 1960s. After 1967 and
the fall of the West Bank and Gaza Strip under Israeli military
rule, child mortality continued downward. But, as Alan Hill
pointed out, the magnitude of the improvement cannot be estimated
because of inadequate data (32). What is important here is that
the consequences of Israeli military occupation on the health of
the population in general, and the three villages in particular,
were various and contradictory. As is the case in all the
occupied areas, the villages have, since 1967, been suffering
from neglect, economic stagnation, the lack of such basic
services as curative and preventive village health projects and
the inadequacy of such other services as state schools (33).
Increased labour income combined with remittances from migrant
workers living in the Gulf to produce improvements in the
population's nutritional intake and a generalised rise in the
standard of living. These changes, in conjunction with the
rising educational level, especially of women, explain the
reduction in childhood mortality throughout the 1970s. This
reduction has been achieved not because of, but despite, Israeli
military rule. Despite occupation policies, the imperatives of
the Israeli economy resulted in unintended consequences. In the

three villages, the unintended consequences have included improved income and reduced deaths. Yet even then, these improvements have lagged behind improvements in other Arab countries, such as Jordan, for instance.

The costs of such improvements have been very high indeed. Better living conditions came at the expense of complete subordination and dependency on Israel for livelihood, and at the expense of the loss of political and human rights. But the impact of Israeli occupation has been uneven, affecting different groups in different ways, and always depending on the needs and priorities of the occupier. These improvements remain temporary in nature and could be reversed, depending on the state of the Israeli and Gulf economies.

The conclusion is not that Israeli military occupation is "good for your health". Nor is it the case that this pattern of improvement is found everywhere in the occupied areas. The impact of military occupation on the Jordan Valley has been to create a much more drastic and severe hazard to life and health than elsewhere in the occupied territories. The conclusion is that the policies of an occupying regime do not necessarily coincide with their economic and social consequences, including their impact on health conditions. While one might condemn Israel's occupation policies in terms of their negative impact on living conditions in general, one must also be aware of the specificity of these policies' consequences in particular settings.

NOTES

1. A saying denoting the promise in marriage of a girl infant at birth. 'A form of child betrothal'. See Granqvist, 1931, op cit, pp. 23-32.

2. Fertility and Crude Birth Rate calculations followed the Estimation of Fertility From Information on Children Ever Born Classified by Duration of Marriage method and were based on data obtained for currently married women. See Manual X, op cit, pp. 64-69.

3. Ibid, p. 69.

4. Health and Health Services, op cit, p. 4.

5. Hill, op cit, pp. 304-308.

6. Ibid.

7. Granqvist, 1931, op cit, p. 44.

8. Ibid, p. 45.

9. Ibid, p. 41.

10. Meillasoux, C, 'The Economic Bases of Demographic Reproduction: From the Domestic Mode of Production to Wage-Earnings', Journal of Peasant Studies, vol II, no 1, 1983, pp. 50-61.

11. See Owen, op cit.

12. Manual X, op cit, p. 62.

13. Hilma Granqvist's Artas is a case in point. Also look at Robertson, J S & Sheard, A V, 'Altered Sex Ratio After an Outbreak of Hepatitis', The Lancet, vol 1, 1973, pp. 532-534.

14. Calculation of q_x - the probability of dying between birth and exact age x - followed the Brass method/Trussel Version/ West model of childhood mortality estimation from information on children ever born and children surviving by duration of marriage, Manual X, op cit, pp. 81-85.

15. Nadarjah, T, 'The Transition from Higher Female to Higher Male Mortality in Sri Lanka', Population and Development Review, no. 2, June, 1983; Naphanson, C, 'Sex, Illness and Medical Care: A Review of Data, Theory and Method', Social Science and Medicine, vol 11, 1980, p. 13.

16. Look at, for instance, el-Badri, M A, 'Higher Female than Male Mortality in Some Countries of South Asia: A Digest',

Journal of American Statistical Association, vol 64, 1969, pp. 1234-1244.

17. Hamoud, E & Esmat, I, 'Studies in Foetal and Infant Mortality II: Differences in Mortality by Sex and Race', *American Journal of Public Health*, vol 55, no 8, 1965, p. 1156.

18. Waldron, I, 'Sex Differences in Human Mortality: The Role of the Genetic Factor', *Social Science and Medicine*, vol 17, no 6, 1983, pp. 321-33; Waldron, I, 'Sex Differences in Illness Incidence, Prognosis and Mortality: Issues and Evidence', *Social Science and Medicine*, vol 17, no 17, 1983, pp. 1107-1123.

19. el-Badri, op cit, p. 1238.

20. Waldron, I, 'Sex Differences in Human Mortality', op cit, p. 321.

21. All the calculations of infant and childhood mortality followed the steps delineated in *Manual X*, op cit, pp. 81-85.

22. This information was obtained from Frederic Shorter, The Population Council, Cairo, Egypt.

23. Schmelz et al, op cit, pp. 75-77.

24. Blacker, J G, Hill, A & Moser, K, *Mortality Levels and Trends in Jordan Estimated from the Results of the 1976 Fertility Survey*, World Fertility Survey Scientific Reports no 47, International Statistics Institude, Voorburg, Netherlands, 1983, p. 20.

25. Grosse, R, 'Interrelation Between Health and Population: Observations Derived from Field Experience', *Social Science and Medicine*, vol 14C, 1980, pp. 99-120.

26. Agbonifo, P O, 'The State of Health as a Reflection of the Level of Development of a Nation', *Social Science and Medicine*, vol 17, no 24, 1983, pp. 2003-2006.

27. Grosse, op cit, pp. 100-102, and Knowles, J, 'Health, Population and Development', *Social Science and Medicine*, vol 14C, 1980, pp. 67-70.

28. Hill, op cit, pp. 301-304.

29. Winikoff, B, & Brown, G, 'Nutrition, Population and Health: Theoretical and Practical Issues', *Social Science and Medicine*, vol 14C, 1980, pp. 171-178; Grosse, op cit;Knowles, op cit; Edmonston, B and Andes, N, 'Community Vari-ations in Infant and Child Mortality in Peru', *Journal of Epidemiology and Community Health*, vol 37, 1983, pp. 121-126.

30. Leigh, J P, 'Direct and Indirect Effects of Education on Health', <u>Social Science and Medicine</u>, vol 17, no 4, 1983, pp. 227-234; Barnes, D et al, 'Rural Literacy and Agricultural Development: Cause or Effect', <u>Rural Sociology</u>, vol 47, no 2, 1982, pp. 251-271; Colclough, C, 'The Impact of Primary Schooling on Economic Development: A Review of the Evidence', <u>World Development</u>, vol 10, no 3, 1982, pp. 167-185.

31. Manderson, L, 'These are Modern Times: Infant Feeding Practices in Peninsular Malaysia', <u>Social Science and Medicine</u>, vol 18, no 1, 1984, pp. 47-54.

32. Hill, op cit, pp. 302-303.

33. Look at, for instance, Benvenisti, op cit, and Graham-Brown, S, <u>Education</u>, op cit, pp. 62-79.

CHAPTER SIX

WOMEN, WEALTH, EDUCATION AND HEALTH

Wealth and Education

Although the married women in these communities had similar living standards, differences did exist and were based in part on the wealth status of families and the educational levels of women in the household. Women from wealthier households tended to be more educated, to live in larger dwellings, to possess more household amenities, to eat better foods and to visit health facilities more frequently than the others. Of 269 or 80% of the total number of married women in the reproductive age, 15% belonged to households categorised by informants as wealthy, 70% were in the middle income group, and the rest were poor by village standards. The presence of facilities considered important for health (piped water supply, latrine and refrigerator) was positively related to wealth. Wealthier households tended to have at least two of these facilities while the poorer ones tended to have either one or none (Table 6.1).

TABLE 6.1

HOUSEHOLD AMENITIES AND FACILITIES BY WEALTH STATUS
(Piped Water, Latrines and Refrigerators)

| Wealth Status of Household | Presence of amenities and facilities | | | Total % |
	None %	One %	Two or more %	
High	7	29	64	100
Medium	19	49	38	100
Low	17	54	29	100

Total Households: 269

Chi square: 12.218   p = 0.05

The same positive association was found between the presence of these facilities and the number of migrant workers abroad (Table 6.2). But this association is slightly more difficult to interpret. It could be that migrant remittances allow for the presence of these facilities at home. It could also be that the exposure of the migrants to the outside world encourages them to

improve their general conditions at home. But it could also be
that wealthier households can afford to send migrants abroad to
generate more wealth while the poorer ones cannot.

TABLE 6.2

HOUSEHOLD FACILITIES AND AMENITIES
(Piped Water, Latrines and Refrigerators)
BY THE PRESENCE OF MIGRANTS

Household Migrants	Presence of Facilities			Total
	None %	One %	Two or more %	
None	20	43	37	100
One	11	47	42	100
Two or more	0	31	69	100

Total households: 269

Chi square: 14.25   p = 0.01

In general, wealth status was associated with better health
behaviour. Wealthy women tended to more actively seek pre- and
post-natal care, keep their drinking-water containers covered,
and keep their houses cleaner than others. Wealthier women gave
birth to their children in the hospital far more often than did
women from the middle income and poor categories (Table 6.3).
They also introduced foods other than milk earlier. Wealthier
and better educated women, however, also completely weaned their
children off breastmilk earlier and faster than others, suggesting that wealth and education can also negatively influence
health behaviour. A significantly larger number of wealthier
women used powdered milk and ready-made weaning foods (mostly
Cerelac by Nestle) to feed their infants than did women from
other wealth categories (Table 6.4).

TABLE 6.3

PLACE OF BIRTH OF CHILDREN BY WEALTH STATUS OF HOUSEHOLDS

Wealth Status of Households	Birth Place		Total %
	Hospital %	Home %	
High	80	20	100
Medium	53	47	100
Low	51	49	100

Total children: 212

Chi square: 7.81   p = 0.05

TABLE 6.4

CHILD-FEEDING PRACTICES BY WEALTH STATUS OF HOUSEHOLDS

Child-Feeding Practices	Household Wealth Status in %		
	High	Medium	Low
Breast-Feeding only	20	47	49
Mixed Feeding (breast and powdered milk)	80	53	51
Total	100	100	100

Total children: 212

          Chi square: 7.81   p = 0.05

Weaning on Cerelac	76	52	52
Weaning on home-made foods	24	48	48
Total	100	100	100

Total children: 208

          Chi square: 5.77   p = 0.05

The level of education of mothers correlated well with their wealth status. These effects could have been partially in-fluenced by age; women in these communities were rapidly increasing their educational attainment (see also Appendix 6). But there was no correlation between wealth and age; young women in these communities could as easily be wealthy as older women. And it was the wealthier women who were significantly better educated (Table 6.5). Although educational levels of women and access to schooling had improved for all women, wealth status appeared to be a determining factor.

TABLE 6.5

EDUCATIONAL LEVELS OF MARRIED WOMEN BY WEALTH STATUS OF HOUSEHOLDS

Educational level of Married Women in Years of Schooling	Wealth Status of Households			Total %
	High %	Medium %	Low %	
None	9	76	15	100
1-5	20	58	22	100
6 or more	25	64	11	100

Total women: 265

          Chi square: 12.319   p = 0.05

The impact of wealth on certain aspects of life and behaviour that influence health status appears to be contradictory. Better living environment, more facilities, better food and higher levels of education should provide the medium through which good health is achieved for the entire family. But the association of wealth with the increased use of powdered milk and early complete weaning off breast milk provide the basis for an unhealthy childhood and an increased risk of death. Before explaining this contradictory pattern and its impact on children's health, it is necessary to examine the effects of education on health behaviour.

Important differences in health and feeding behaviour were, in general, associated with the mothers' level of education but not the fathers' or any other members' of the household. The presence of internal latrines in households tended to increase somewhat with increasing education of mothers: 9% of the mothers with no education, 10% of those with 1-5 years and 22% of those with more than five years of education had internal latrines in their dwellings. A stronger relationship was noted for covering drinking-water containers: 49% of the mothers with no education, 61% of mothers with 1-5 years of school and 76% of mothers with six or more years of school had their drinking-water containers well covered during the interview session. Women with more education tended to seek prenatal care more often than those who had less or none. Of a total of 246 women who had experienced at least one pregnancy, 33% of those with no education, 39% of those with 1-5 years of school and 71% of those who had six or more years of education went to a prenatal clinic at least once during their most recent pregnancy (Appendix 6). No significant relation was found between the birthplace (hospital versus home delivery) of children under three years old and their weaning and feeding patterns and mother's age, although a slight trend towards more hospital births and increased use of powdered milk and ready-made weaning foods was noted as the mother's age decreased. Educated mothers, however, consistently had higher rates of hospital births, powdered milk, and ready-made weaning food use as well as early and complete weaning (Table 6.4).

Thus, as is the case with wealth status, the educational level of mothers as a determinant of health status and the risk of death of children manifested itself on health and feeding behaviour in different ways. A general improvement in the sanitary environment in the home and in sanitary habits followed increased education along with other determinants such as wealth. But the use of artificial milk and weaning foods also rose with increased education.

These findings, of course, are not surprising. For the decline in breastfeeding among Third World women has been noted for some years (1). The importance of breastfeeding children, especially during the critical first few months of life, has also been known for some time. Breast milk supports growth better than other types of milk because it provides infants with a balanced ratio of protein and energy (2). It also provides immunological protection, especially in situations where sanitary conditions are poor. Indeed, recent evidence indicates that this immunological protection and defence against infection is responsive to the pathogens present in the immediate environment of the mother and infant (3). Breastfeeding, in addition, is more hygienic, and does not expose the infant to the additional risk of contaminated food that accompanies the use of powdered milk, especially under unsanitary conditions. This risk factor associated with the use of powdered milk applies equally well to such weaning foods as the Cerelac being used in the three villages, since they, too, must be reconstituted with water. Finally, breastfeeding has an influence on fertility (4) that could significantly affect infant mortality (5) and probably morbidity as well.

TABLE 6.6

BIRTH PLACE AND FEEDING PRACTICES BY EDUCATIONAL
LEVELS OF MOTHERS
(Children Under the Age of Three Years)

Birth Place of Child and Feeding Practices	Educational Level of Mother		
	None %	1-5 Years %	6 Years or more %
Hospital birth	47	64	76
Home birth	53	36	24
Total	100	100	100

Chi square: 4.99   p = 0.005

Breast-feeding only	51	42	33
Mixed feeding (powdered and breast milk)	49	58	67
Total	100	100	100

Chi square: 4.99   p = 0.08

Weaning on Cerelac	47	57	67
Weaning on home-made foods	53	43	33
Total	100	100	100

Chi square: 6.10   p = 0.05

Complete weaning off mother's milk under six months	46	46	68
Complete weaning off mother's milk over six months	54	54	32
Total	100	100	100

Chi square: 6.05   p = 0.05

The impact of this change in feeding behaviour among women in underdeveloped countries has been no less than dramatic. A Chilean study reported higher mortality among infants artificial-ly fed in the first three months of life. Similar findings were obtained with regard to morbidity in several countries including the affluent societies, where standards of hygiene are relatively good. In an Iranian village it was found that the majority of the children found to be nutritionally normal were breastfed. The rest of the normal children were being fed a mixture of artificial and breast milk (6). In a Micronesian village, the occurrence of illness serious enough to warrant hospitalisation was found to be associated with exclusive bottle-feeding in the first year of life (7). In Israel, a prospective study of a group of middle-class Jewish women revealed that exclusively breastfed infants experienced significantly fewer symptoms of disease than those partially or wholly fed artificially. It also revealed a positive correlation between breastfeeding duration and a diminished number of children's illnesses. The study concluded that even middle-class, well-educated women benefited from breastfeeding as a practice with protective effects for both them and their children (8). Yet despite the hazards, artificial feeding continues to be a popular practice. Industrialisation, urbanisation, contact with bearers of Western industrial culture, mother's work outside the home, women's educational level, the breakup of joint family systems and the influence of marketing and advertisement have all been implicated as factors influencing breastfeeding practices (6).

In the three villages, structural changes have had an impact on economic and social life, as well as on health and feeding practices. Improved incomes have led to a generalised change in consumption patterns, not only with regard to food and feeding. Industrialisation or urbanisation did not mediate in this case, for the West Bank urban, industrial and overall economic infrastructures have essentially remained stagnant since the Israeli military occupation began. The village economy has also remained so, despite an increased purchasing power at the individual level. Purchasing power has manifested itself in increased facilities in the homes and in ownership of amenities. It has also manifested itself in an increase in the consumption of purchased foods, especially those of animal origins. But it has primarily manifested itself in the sprouting of newly built houses on the outskirts of the villages.

Thus, wage relations and the growing importance of money as a mark of status carried with them a trend towards conspicuous purchases. The higher the wealth status, the more spacious the house, the more household amenities, the larger the house, the more artificial feeding, which became associated with status and prestige. The more educated the women, the more conscious of status and prestige and the need to appear "modern" they became. Wage relations, however, were not the only factor that precipi- tated these changes. Advertisements and marketing and the promotion of artificial feeding by some members of the health care professional establishment were important factors as well. Of 127 women asked to explain the reason they were feeding their children powdered milk, especially at an early age, 45% said their milk was insufficient, 16% said their milk had dried up, 13% gave pregnancy as a cause, 2% implicated wage work as a cause, and the rest gave such other reasons as breast abscess, or infection, and maternal illness. When the women were asked how they decided that their milk was insufficient, almost a third said that their doctor told them so. The other two thirds were equally divided between the television and their friends, neighbours and relatives as the way through which they had found out about the use of powdered milk for infant feeding.

Contraception: Another Factor Influencing Fertility and Health

Attitudes towards birth control and the use of birth control methods were practically impossible to discuss with the women of these communities. Not only were they unwilling to divulge information regarding whether they were actually controlling their fertility, they were generally reluctant to respond to questions about their satisfaction with their family size. This is understandable in terms of the strong pro-natalist social pressure exercised by the presence of other women members of the family, or friends and neighbours. Privacy as an alternative was practically impossible, given the general circumstances of village life. In the face of this situation, the majority of women responded to the family size inquiry by stating that children are a ni'meh (a gift from God), and that the more of them the better. In fact, however, Birzeit health clinic records showed that there were some 25 to 30 women from these communities taking birth control pills in a sporadic fashion. The clinic included a family planning programme that provided birth control pills free of charge, for the purpose of child spacing and not fertility reduction. This distinction is important since in the occupied territories fertility reduction is negatively regarded on political, religious and customary grounds.

The women were willing to respond to questions about their knowledge of contraceptive methods, however, for those questions were not incriminating. Responding to them did not necessarily mean contraceptive use. Of a total of 272 married women, 24% did not know of any contraceptive method. Of the rest, 53% knew of birth control pills, 20% of intrauterine devices, 17% of tubal ligation and the rest knew of other methods such as diaphragms, birth control suppositories, condoms and other traditional methods, which appeared to include both harmful and harmless means of fertility control. Among the harmless means was swallowing a whole grain of coffee immediately after birth as a way of protecting the newly delivered mother against an immediate pregnancy. Among the probably harmful means was the insertion of a piece of cotton wool dipped into olive oil into the vaginal canal after intercourse. In general, older women knew of birth control pills and tubal ligation while younger women knew of intrauterine devices. Those who had more education tended to know both birth control pills and intrauterine devices, while those with no schooling at all seemed to know of withdrawal and tubal ligation.

Fertility levels have been known to be influenced by an array of factors. Those include health and nutritional status, mortality rates, feeding practices, and educational levels of mothers, among other influences (10). It is thought that improved nutritional status, a reduction in the death rate and increased educational levels of mothers all ultimately work towards a reduction in fertility. According to the "child survival hypothesis", high levels of childhood mortality cause an increase in fertility, since parents continue to attempt to achieve their desired family size so long as death prevents them from reaching this stage. Thus, a decline in mortality should result in a declining fertility. A large number of studies, however, have shown that such declines in mortality were not followed by a fully compensating decline in fertility (11). This and other criticisms led to the refinement of this hypothesis. It is now believed that parents are most likely to respond to improved chances of children surviving by further reducing fertility, where health is improving and fertility is already falling – but sill lagging behind mortality declines – and where contraceptives are accessible (12). Although this hypothesis does explain, in part, high fertility in underdeveloped countries, it remains problematic, because it fails to take into consideration other influences on fertility that may be of considerable importance. Of those that could be mentioned here are the effects of wage labour and relations, the impact of the alienation of people from the land and the effects of colonial aggression and wars on fertility.

What is disturbing about the fertility debate, however, is its emphasis on fertility reduction without adequate assessment of safety or risk of contraceptive use. In addition, although decreased fertility and increased birth spacing have been shown to result in significant declines in infant mortality, which is often used as a justification for population control programmes, it is really not clear whether this reduced mortality is due to the effects of decreased fertility, or to generalised economic and social changes that have accompanied this reduction. It would seem reasonable to suggest that improved incomes and living conditions and the general increased sanitary properties of the environment are overriding factors in the determination of mortality, as McKeown has shown for industrialising countries (14). If this should be the case for underdeveloped countries, as it appears to be at the moment (15), then improved living conditions and incomes of the people of underdeveloped countries and their liberation would also be overriding factors that determine mortality and ultimately, fertility.

The fertility picture in the three villages is complicated by many influences. Wage labour, land alienation and colonial aggression are influences that could induce an increased fertility response. As discussed earlier, financial and social security in the form of children, as opposed to land, does provide the justification for parents to desire many of them. Reduced infant mortality and increased educational levels of women could, however, theoretically create an opposite effect. It is doubtful, though, that they would. The evidence does suggest that infant mortality is declining, but its level is still substantially and unacceptably high. Ninety-one deaths for every 1000 births means that the majority of parents in these communities, have experienced the death of at least one child. Children's deaths are very much part of the experience of these communities and as long as the infant mortality levels remain at such a high level, despite the suggested improvement, it is highly likely that fertility will remain high as well.

The important question to raise here relates to the justifications for fertility control and population programmes in the Palestinian context at large. Child spacing may admittedly be of benefit to both mother and child, but a concentration on its effects on health, to the exclusion of more important influences, deflects attention from the political and economic contexts within which ill health and death occur to begin with. I am not suggesting that contraceptive methods should not be available to Palestinian parents. The crux of the argument, rather, is that efforts to solve the problems of ill health and death ought to be directed towards the removal of the major causes. It is not the question of the right to contraception, nor of whether family planning programmes ought to exist in the occupied territories. Clearly, family planning programmes can be of benefit, if they exist in conjunction with other attempts to solve the population's health problems. But their impact on health will continue to remain very limited as long as the major causes of ill health continue to prevail, and as long as material conditions necessitate the bearing of many children. Palestinians in the occupied territories do not have a population problem. On the contrary, they are continually faced with the problem of depopulation. It is the right to remain on their own land and the right of self-determination ·they need, not population control.

Anaemia Rates Among Married Women

It is widely recognised today that anaemia among women of childbearing age in Third World countries - especially during pregnancy - is a common, indeed major, nutritional deficiency, affecting the health of both mothers and their children. The most common type of anaemia is due to iron deficiency. Iron intake is to a large extent determined by the presence of iron in the staple food consumed, but also by the presence of adequate quantities of protein in food needed for iron absorption (16). Women of reproductive age are generally at a higher risk of becoming anaemic than the rest of the population. Biological (menstruation and pregnancy) and social (low status and poverty, leading to the ingestion of less and lower quality foods) causes the nutritional deprivation which creates this anaemia.

The rate of low haematocrit levels (indicators of the haemoglobin concentration in blood and the prevalence of anaemia) was found to be not as high as the rates for some underdeveloped countries. Of the 250 married women of childbearing age who had their haematocrit level tested, 17% had haematocrit levels lower than

36 or haemoglobin levels below 12 grams (that is, were found to be anaemic). The prevalence of low haematocrit levels did not correlate with a range of possible determinants, including educational levels of mothers and the receipt of prenatal care, although there appeared to be a tendency towards increasing prevalence with increasing age (Table 6.7) up until the ages of 40 years or over. This trend is understandable given that successive and multiple pregnancies are more likely to occur among women in their twenties and thirties than among women in their forties, and given that pregnancy is a major cause of anaemia among women of childbearing age. Haematocrit levels were found to be significantly related to pregnancy; 39% of those who were pregnant had a haematocrit level under 36 while only 12% of those who were not pregnant had the same low level (Chi square: 15.8; p = 0.0001). The same strong correlation was found between low haematocrit levels and the proportions of children dead; only 12% of those who had not experienced children's deaths had a low haematocrit level, while 23% of those who had experienced more than 20% of deaths among children had low haematocrit levels (Chi square 9.99; p = 0.05). A trend of increasingly low levels with decreasing wealth was discernable as well (Table 6.8).

TABLE 6.7

HAEMATOCRIT LEVELS BY AGE
MARRIED WOMEN OF CHILDBEARING AGE ONLY

| | Haematocrit Levels | | |
Age of women	Under 36	36 or over	Total
15-19	10%	90%	100%
20-29	15%	85%	100%
30-39	21%	79%	100%
40-49	14%	86%	100%

Total women: 250

TABLE 6.8

HAEMATOCRIT LEVELS BY WEALTH STATUS OF HOUSEHOLDS
MARRIED WOMEN OF CHILDBEARING AGE ONLY

| | Haematocrit Levels | | |
Wealth status	Under 36	Over 36	Total
High	13%	87%	100%
Medium	16%	84%	100%
Low	21%	79%	100%

Total women: 250

The rate of low haematocrit levels during pregnancy among the women tested in these communities seems to be close to the rates obtained for pregnant women in certain areas of Brazil and

Nigeria (17). Although anaemia among women from underdeveloped countries - especially during pregnancy - is highly prevalent, exceptions do exist and depend on a variety of influences including diet and fertility. In the three villages, although the fertility rate was high, the village diet had been improving considerably in terms of the inclusion of foods of animal origins which contain good quantities of iron and protein. At the same time, despite the increased purchasing power of individual households, the village diet was still based on wheat bread as a staple, and rich in fresh green vegetables and a variety of pulses considered good and cheap sources of iron. But as we have noted before, food consumption patterns have been changing, and the ingestion of such manufactured foods as white bread, biscuits and soft drinks, among other items, has been on the increase. Whether these foods will ultimately replace the traditional and basically nutritious diet remains to be seen. So far, this mix of the old vegetable-based diet and the increasing ability of households to purchase foods of animal origin appears to have had positive effects, to the extent that this could be judged based on the haematocrit data. But, these very tentative remarks should be treated with caution; the picture of change in food consumption patterns is vague and conflicting, and requires systematic and extended examination.

NOTES

1. Look at, for instance, Ebrahim, G J, <u>Breastfeeding: The
    Biological Option</u>, Macmillan, London, 1978; Jeliffe, D B &
    Jeliffe, E P, <u>Human Milk in the Modern World</u>, Oxford
    University Press, Oxford, 1979; Ebrahim, G J, <u>Child Health
    in a Changing Environment</u>, Macmillan, London, 1982, pp. 27-
    35.

2. Ebrahim, <u>Child Health</u>, op cit, p. 26.

3. Grosse, op cit, p. 105.

4. Meldrum, B & DiDomenico, C, 'Production and Reproduction,
    Women and Breastfeeding: Some Nigerian Examples', <u>Social
    Science and Medicine</u>, Vol 16, 1982, pp. 1247-1251.

5. Grosse, op cit, p. 105.

6. Plank, S & Milanesi, M, 'Infant Feeding and Infant Mortality
    in Chile', <u>Bulletin of the World Health Organisation</u>, Vol
    48, pp. 201-220, 1973, cited in Ebrahim, <u>Child Health</u>, op
    cit, p. 48; Cunningham, A S, 'Morbidity in Breast Fed and
    Artificially Fed Infants', <u>Journal of Pediatrics</u>, Vol 95,
    1979, pp. 685-689; Djazayery, A et al, 'Assessment of the
    Nutritional Status of Pre-School Children in Mahabad Rural
    Areas', <u>Journal of Tropical Pediatrics</u>, Vol 29, 1983,
    p. 331.

7. Marshall, L & Marshall, M, 'Infant Feeding and Infant
    Illness in a Micronesian Village', <u>Social Science and
    Medicine</u>, Vol 14B, 1980, p. 33.

8. Patti, M, et al, 'Episodes of Illness in Breastfed and
    Bottlefed Infants in Jerusalem', <u>Israel Journal of Medical
    Science</u>, Vol 20, no 5, 1984, pp. 395-399.

9. Manderson, op cit, pp. 47-57; Igun, U A, 'Child Feeding
    Habits in a Situation of Social Change: The Case of
    Maiduguri, Nigeria', <u>Social Science and Medicine</u>, Vol 16,
    1982, pp. 769-781; Dev, K A et al, 'Breast Feeding Practices
    in Urban Slums and Rural Areas of Varansi', <u>Journal of
    Tropical Pediatrics</u>, Vol 28, no 2, 1982, pp. 89-92.

10. Rehan, N, 'Knowledge, Attitude and Practice of Family
    Planning in Hausa Women', <u>Social Science and Medicine</u>, Vol
    18, no 10, 1984, pp. 839-844; Winikoff, B & Brown, G,
    'Nutrition Population and Health: Theoretical and Practical
    Issues', <u>Social Science and Medicine'</u>, Vol 14C, 1980, pp.
    171-176; Meldrum & DiDomenico, op cit, pp. 1247-1251;
    Grosse, op cit, p. 10.

11. Winkoff & Brown, op cit, p. 173.

12.   Ibid, p. 174.

13.   Ibid, p. 174.

14.   McKeown, T, <u>Modern Rise</u>, op cit.

15.   Look at, for instance, Wood, C, 'The Political Economy of Infant Mortality in Sao Paulo, Brazil', <u>International Journal of Health Services</u>, Vol 12, no 2, 1982, p. 215; Navarro, V, 1982, op cit; Doyal, L, op cit.

16.   Ebrahim, G S, <u>Pediatric Practice in Developing Countries</u>, Macmillan, London, 1981, pp. 68-69.

17.   Salzano, A C et al, 'Prevelencia de anaemia no ciclo genstacional em dois estados do nordeste Brasileiro, Pernambuso e Paraba (Prevalence of anaemia among pregnant women in the Brazilian State of Pernambuco and Paraiba)', <u>Revista Brasileira de Pesquisas Medicas e Biologicas</u>, Vol 13, 1980, pp. 211-214, cited in <u>Salus: Low-Cost Rural Health Care and Health Manpower Training</u>, International Development Research Centre, Ottawa, 1984; Chukudebelu, W & Obi, G, 'Anaemia in Pregnancy in Nigerians', <u>Nigerian Medical Journal</u>, Vol 9, no 2, 1979, pp. 221-223.

CHAPTER SEVEN

CHILDREN OF THE WEST BANK

Life in these village communities normally offers children a lifestyle similar to that elsewhere in Third World villages. They tend to be much freer to move around the village than town or urban dwellers are. Nature provides both their toys and playground. Children spend most of their day outside playing with twigs, mud, coca cola cans, plastic bags and stones, among other natural and synthetic items. They are left unattended, barefoot and almost always dirty. They are free to move around without fear, and no one prohibits them when curiosity instructs them to tear an object apart to examine it: such objects, if found, have already been deemed useless. The evidence of a changing consumption pattern in toys, as in food and other goods, is mounting, however. These days bicycles are fashionable, as are wristwatches for boys, but only for those lucky enough to have a family member working in the Gulf. The favourite toy of all is the leftover vehicle tyre. This offers a variety of uses; it can be made into a swing, or rolled downhill. But its truly remarkable property is its inflammability. On days of national upheaval, roadblocks are mounted and tyres are burnt, to mark the participation of even the smallest villages in the political events.

Young boys and girls ranging from those who can barely walk up until the ages of nine or ten play together without regard to distinctions based on age or gender. Nor are distinctions based on class or status apparent either. Everyone seems to play together. What appears to be the factor defining who plays with which groups is the distance between homes. But by age nine or ten things begin to change. Girls and boys alike begin to assume male and female roles. Although girls tend to assume some responsibility for housework very early on, they tend to be given full responsibilities at around this age. Boys then begin to consider wage labour and some in fact do work in Israeli farms, picking fruits and vegetables during their summer holidays from school. It is at this age that one can first witness a definite division of labour between the sexes and their separation into different societies.

Such a seemingly ordinary life, however, is periodically and sometimes very dramatically disrupted by factors coming from out-side the village. Imprisonment, torture, death, deportation, house demolition, land confiscation, settler violence, tear gas, bullets and military checkpoints are fundamental events that help form the life experience of the villages' children. For, while these communities do tend to lead a relatively sheltered life, they are not spared the impact of Israeli military rule. In one village, the extended, or life imprisonment of one or more younger members of families was rather common. All three had been affected by land confiscations. The proximity of these villages to Birzeit University exposed children to concrete stories of settler violence, shooting and other forms of violence. Children in these villages respond to these events, when appropriate, with their own form of resistance. Their adverse reaction to military occupation has manifested itself in the form of stone-throwing capabilities. These begin in early childhood, practised on donkeys and chicken very much as part of what is normally done by children and sometimes by adults. Come preparatory school, however, when children must travel to town for schooling, their stone-throwing capabilities truly develop, along with their political consciousness. It is generally then that the object of their stone-throwing interest becomes the Israeli army or settlers. Their adverse reaction to military occupation expresses itself in the form of resistance by stone-throwing directed against anything that smells of occupier. If success is to be judged by prominence in the Israeli media (1), these activities certainly have proven to be a success. Such activities have also, unfortunately, been used by the military to justify collective punishment measures against many refugee camp and village communities (such as states of siege, mass detention, harassment of adult males, and so on).

The adverse effects of military occupation on the mental health of Palestinian children is not yet understood. There has not been one single systematic attempt to unfold the problem. But indications of a problem exist, mostly in the form of tentative remarks made by parents and schoolteachers. Children play a game called "army" in which they set up checkpoints. There are also many reports of sleep disturbances and nightmares. One parent/teacher at Birzeit University was desperate enough about her daughter's persistent nightmares and fears to go and plead with an Israeli soldier to tell the daughter that he would not kill either her or her mother. The schoolgirl poisoning incidents of the spring of 1983 appear to be a manifestation of the problem as well. About 1000 schoolchildren from several districts of the West Bank were admitted to hospitals with similar symptoms of toxicity, all within a few days. But no firm proof of toxicity was obtained by Palestinian health professionals or by the Center for Disease Control's team of experts invited by the State of Israel to investigate the cases. Although Palestinian health professionals believe that toxicity was responsible for the symptoms some of the schoolgirls suffered, they also believe that many of the cases were actually psychological in origin, set against a background of anxiety and stress caused by the political situation. These conclusions were confirmed by the Center for Disease Control's team of experts (2). What those incidents indicate is the need to take seriously the problems of mental health under the impact of military occupation.

Although the three communities are not at the centre of political life and the attention of the Israeli military, they do receive their share of problems. The water crisis is one example of the complications created by the political situation.   Guerilla fighter arrests and night raids by the army are not altogether unknown, for, unlike what is perhaps commonly believed, many who have joined the resistance movement are of rural origins. Rather than have to deal with the military government, the villagers prefer at times to have as little connection with the outside world as possible. For example, in response to the question of whether the villagers would like to have a phone connection installed in their village, the Mukhtar of one (apparently oblivious to the substantial difficulties of obtaining one) responded:

> What? Do you want us to have a phone connection with Ramallah so that the military governor could then call me and order me to send the community members for interrogation or imprisonment? No, no, we do not want this headache, let them do their dirty work for themselves.

The Nutritional Status Assessment of Children

There were 222 children under 3 years old in the three villages. Forty-five per cent had no other siblings under the age of three, 48% were one of two, and 7% were one of three siblings under that age.   There was a strong association between the number of children under this age and the education of their mothers (Table 7.1). Mothers with six or more years of schooling had either one or two children in this age category. A similar trend of decreasing number of children under 3 years old with increasing wealth was noted (Appendix 7).   As expected, the majority of children under this age had mothers whose ages were between 20 and 39 years (Appendix 7).

TABLE 7.1

NUMBER OF CHILDREN UNDER THREE YEARS BY EDUCATION OF MOTHERS

Number of children	Percentage of education category		
	No education	1-5 years	6 years or more
1	52	25	45
2	42	59	55
3	6	16	0

Total: 212 (10 cases missing)
Chi square: 18.4 $p = 0.001$

We measured the weights and lengths/heights of 209 children under 3 years old. Forty-six per cent of these were females. Nutritional status was expressed by the weight for length for age classification of Mclaren and Read (3) (Table 7.2). The overall rate of malnutrition was 41%. A trend of increasing malnutrition with age was observable up until the end of the age of weaning (0-23 months). As expected, cases of moderate malnutrition seemed to concentrate especially around the ages of 6 to 23 months, or the ages of weaning. There were very few cases of severe malnutrition and nutritional dwarfism (an indication of past malnutrition). These results were similar to those obtained by Mclaren and Read for children coming from a population of low socio-economic status in a Beirut suburb (Bourj al-Barajneh) in 1975 (4). They were also similar to the results obtained for a group of Iranian pre-school children in 1983. Although the trends were similar, both the rate and the severity of malnutrition was higher among the Iranian than the Palestinian children who were the subject of the project (5). Since both the Lebanese and Iranian studies utilised the same method of nutritional status assessment as that of this research project they are useful for comparison purposes.

TABLE 7.2

NUTRITIONAL STATUS BY AGE OF CHILD - BOTH SEXES

Nutritional status	0-5 months	6-11 months	12-23 months	24-35 months	Total
			percentages		
Obese	4	0	0	0	0
Overweight	10	3	0	0	2
Normal	55	51	55	63	57
Mild malnutrition	17	15	14	22	20
Moderate malnutrition	7	27	14	4	13
Severe malnutrition	7	2	4	3	5
Nutritional dwarf	0	2	4	3	3
Total malnutrition	31	46	45	37	41

Total children: 209

A breakdown of nutritional status by sex revealed a significant difference between boys and girls: 32% of the boys and 52% of the girls were malnourished (Table 7.3). Girls were found to constitute 55% of the mild malnutrition category and 70% of the moderate one, although they formed only 46% of the total number of children examined. In addition, girls were found to be more malnourished than boys at all ages. This discrepancy does begin to disappear after the age of weaning, that is, after 2 years old, when children for the most part help themselves from a common container (Appendix 8).

TABLE 7.3

NUTRITIONAL STATUS BY SEX OF CHILD

| | Percentage | |
Nutritional status	Boys	Girls
Obese	1	0
Overweight	3	1
Normal	64	47
Mild malnutrition	17	24
Moderate malnutrition	7	20
Severe malnutrition	5	6
Nutritional dwarf	3	2
Overall malnutrition	32	52
Total children	54(112)	46(97)

Chi square: 7.3   p = 0.1

It is by now well established that nutritional status in early childhood correlates strongly with health status and mortality risk (6). A causal triad, composed of malnutrition, diarrhoeal diseases and respiratory infections, is generally believed to have synergistic effects that can lead to childhood death (7). Moreover, malnutrition in early childhood can have long-lasting effects. Not only can it cause growth retardation and short stature, it can also retard the intellectual growth of children and impair their intellectual performance (8). In general, malnutrition is seen as an indicator of health status, mortality risk and the overall level of development of a nation. Poverty is widely acknowledged as its ultimate determinant. The unexpectedly high overall rate of 41% malnutrition among the children in the three villages points to the need to take this problem into serious consideration when planning for and implementing village health projects. This is so especially in view of the fact that severe and readily identifiable forms of malnutrition such as marasmus and kwashiorkor are uncommon in these communities. The mild and moderate forms predominant there are, then, hidden potential killers and causes of morbidity, especially since they are not readily identifiable. They can easily escape the attention of both parents and health care providers, and ultimately end up causing long-lasting or permanent damage because of the oblique nature of their presentation.

Here, two phenomena require explanation: the first is the existence of malnutrition among children, its causes and determinants; the second is the differential between the sexes. Children are known to be vulnerable to disease during early

childhood.   During this stage, rapid growth imposes specific
nutritional requirements.   Moreover, it is at this stage when the
child is not longer protected by the immunity of breast milk.
Through stimulation, the child's immunological mechanism must
face up to environmental assaults on its own.   Within favourable
environments, children usually experience illnesses and recover
after a brief period.   It is when the general environment
- physical, ecological, or social - is unhealthy that children do
not recover rapidly or well, and are faced with the risk of
death.   Those children who are environmentally vulnerable tend
to be poor, and suffering the consequences of underdevelopment in
their society.

Although age does in part explain the potential risk of malnutrition in the three villages, it does not explain its existence
among some groups and not others, nor does it explain why this
risk has turned into reality.   Although the interdependency of
all the possible nutritional status determinants makes a complete
and   coherent   explanation   very   difficult,   we   nevertheless
attempted to formulate one by examining socio-economic, environmental and behavioural factors known to influence nutritional
status.

Apart from gender, the type of water source found in the child's
dwelling was the only variable that correlated significantly with
nutritional status.   Those who had a piped water supply in their
dwelling had the lowest rate of malnutrition: 14%.   They were
followed by those children whose households had an external
source of running water, where the malnutrition rate was 25%.
Those who did not have any running water and had to rely
completely on cisterns or springs had a 45% rate of malnutrition
(Table 7.4).

TABLE 7.4

NUTRITIONAL STATUS BY WATER SOURCE IN DWELLING

Nutritional status of children	Water source in dwelling		
	Inside Water	Outside Water	No running Water
	----------percentages------------		
Normal	86	75	55
Malnourished	14	25	45

Total children: 203
Chi square: 5.85   p = 0.05

As has been shown previously, the presence or absence of a piped
water supply in dwellings is to some extent determined by wealth
status and the education of mothers.   But these are not the only
important factors.   By far the most important determinant here is
political; that is, the inability of two of these communities to
obtain permission from Israeli military authorities to connect

the villages with the Ramallah-Birzeit running water line. Even
for many of the villagers who could afford to do so, installing
internal pipes, given the existing water sources (cistern and
spring water, both rain-dependent) simply does not make sense;
pipes carry with them the risk of drastically increased use and
the quick exhaustion of supplies. Internal pipes make sense only
when supplies are continuous and assured. Given this major
constraint, one wonders about the value of such activities as
health education when the material conditions that aid the
translation of knowledge into action are absent. It would seem
reasonable to suggest that in the absence of an adequate and safe
source of water, conventional health education remains of limited
use to the inhabitants of these communities.

Although no other statistically significant correlations were
found between the various possible determinants we examined and
nutritional status, some interesting trends and negative
correlations were observable. A negative association was found,
for example, between the presence of internal latrines in the
dwellings and nutritional status. Among children who had
internal latrines, 63% were malnourished. Those whose latrines
were external and those who had none had a 40% rate of malnutrition. These results raise the question of whether internal
latrines may actually pose a hazard to health in situations where
an adequate water supply is lacking. Latrines in proximity to
living areas, given the absence of an effective flushing
mechanism and aided by flies and mosquitos, could in fact
increase the risk of the immediate living environment's being
contaminated with faecal matter. This in turn could increase the
incidence of diarrhoeal diseases and therefore malnutrition among
children.

A trend of increasing malnutrition with decreasing wealth was
observable, where 23% of the high, 44% of the middle and 55% of
the low income groups were found to be malnourished. There was,
however, no relation between either the father's occupation or
the household dependency ratio (the number of economically
inactive members of the family per worker) and nutritional
status. This suggests that wealth and its impact on nutritional
status is a function of more than wage labour locally and in
Israel; family wealth in these communities is the total sum of
revenues obtained from wage labour, remittances from abroad and
land holdings. There was no relation between the age of mothers
and nutritional status; and mothers who were more educated had an
only slightly lower rate of malnutrition among their children
(Appendix 9). This is possibly due to the contradictory effects
of education on health behaviour given the prevailing living
conditions discussed earlier.

In general, questionnaire data on feeding and weaning behaviour
and its impact on the nutritional status of children yielded
vague and far from conclusive results. There was also no
correlation between nutritional status and drinking-water
coverage at home. This may suggest that water contamination
actually occurs prior to the storage of water at home and that,

if further contamination takes place once the water is transported to dwellings, it is of minor importance. Children who were
taken for post-natal care were less malnourished than those who
were not, with 28% and 43% rates of malnutrition respectively.
This suggests that post-natal care of children may have a
positive impact on their nutritional status. There was no clear
correlation between breastfeeding, age of weaning, types of foods
used during the weaning stage, age of complete weaning and the
nutritional status of children (Appendix 9), even though very
slight differences did exist, in favour of those whose mothers
had healthier feeding behaviour.

Though much disagreement currently exists concerning various
determinants of nutritional status, there is agreement on at
least two: the early weaning of children off breastmilk and the
late introduction of foods other than milk into their diet.
Early weaning of children (under the age of 6 months) and the use
of powdered milk and other types of foods instead deprives the
child of a source of immunity (mother's milk) while simultaneously increasing the risk of diarrhoeal diseases and malnutrition as
a result of the ingestion of contaminated artificial milk and
other foods. By the time a child is 6 months old, its immune
system has developed and is better able to defend the child from
environmental pathogens. But by that time also, mother's milk is
no longer capable of fulfilling its nutritional requirements.
The child then needs foods other than milk for adequate survival.
Late introduction of solid foods (after the age of 6 months)
deprives the child of necessary nourishment and can lead to
malnutrition.

Our attempt to understand feeding behaviour and its relation to
malnutrition, morbidity and mortality was made more difficult,
however, by problems of reliability we encountered regarding
questionnaire responses. The majority of women reported that
they introduced foods other than milk at the physiologically
required time, generally no later than the sixth or seventh
month; this should have meant that the late introduction of foods
was not a cause of malnutrition among children in these communities. In fact, however, mothers were observed introducing
foods other than milk too early for a Third World setting and
even among those women who said they exclusively breastfed their
infants, the practice of occasional bottlefeeding was rather
common. This can perhaps explain the presence of malnutrition
among children and the lack of difference in nutritional status
between those who were reported breastfed and those who were
reported mixed fed. But it also raises doubts as to the value of
the questionnaire and interview methods in attempting to
understand the relationship between health and behaviour and the
relationship between knowledge and behaviour. The findings
indicate that the women's responses to questions on feeding
practices are, to some extent, a measure of the level of
knowledge they have concerning proper child feeding. These
responses, however, do not appear to constitute an accurate
reflection of actual practices, and thus are not the appropriate
method through which to pursue an understanding of this problem.

It is not necessarily knowledge of healthy feeding practices but actual behaviour that is the determinant of nutritional status.

If the relationship between health, behaviour and nutritional status is not clear, then the relationship between health behaviour, gender and nutritional status, that is, how gender operates as a determinant in this situation, is even less so. No clear-cut relationships were established between the sex of the child, nutritional status and health and feeding behaviour. There were very small variations in feeding and weaning behaviour that were consistently in favour of males. A decrease in wealth status appeared to have affected the nutritional status of females more than males, suggesting that the impact of decreased family incomes is more adversely reflected on the health of female than male children. Increased education of mothers appeared to have negatively affected females more than males to the extent that the trend towards early complete weaning appeared to be sharper for females (Appendix 10). Yet all of these findings require further research and ultimately leave the problem of nutritional status, behaviour and gender unresolved.

Similar problems concerning the profile of infant feeding practices and the relationship between beliefs and practices have been reported elsewhere (10). It appears that the direct observation of behaviour elicited by ethnographic studies may be the more appropriate tool for the study of behaviour and practices. The relationship between belief and action is complex and modified by an array of factors. In the three villages one would expect a constant modification of behaviour; society is in transition. The educational levels of mothers are increasing, with both positive and negative effects on health and feeding behaviour; wage labour and migration also have an impact on behaviour, in terms of both income levels and a general exposure to "modern" living; needs and aspirations are on the rise and food consumption patterns are being modified by the new material conditions. The basis upon which beliefs and behaviour are founded are changing; but these changes are not uniform and their influences take different directions.

We suspect that it is how mothers respond to their children generally, and not what they do specifically that may explain gender differences in health. We repeatedly saw mothers reconstitute milk powder in ways different from the ways they said they used. Here, too, knowledge and practice were not identical. Although the mothers knew what ought to be done, and partially did what was expected, they did not always do it; they were operating under the constraints of large families, inadequate facilities and limited budgets. During extended visits to households, we noticed that mothers often were more attentive to the needs of their male children. They tended to respond more quickly to their crying, to pay more attention to whether they had eaten or not, and to what and how much they had eaten. Male children and fathers were invariably given the more nutritionally and socially valued foods, such as eggs and meat. The portions male children were alloted also tended to be larger. Although these remarks are tentative, they raise the possibility that the preferential treatment of male children may not operate at the conscious level, but at a level shaped by generalized attitudes affecting behaviour diffusely.   Cause and effect relationships may thus be inappropriate for approaching the problem of gender as a determinant of nutritional status.

Parasites in Children's Stools: Index of Environmental Contamination

The interaction between nutrition and infection is generally known as a major contributor to morbidity and mortality world-wide.   This interaction appears to be mutually aggravating; nutritional deficiencies impair various immune responses and thus contribute to the development of infection.   Infection, in turn, affects the appetite, causes nutrient loss through diarrhoea and vomiting, and impairs the absorption of nutrients from the intestinal tract, among other effects (11).   Infectious diseases are so well correlated with water supplies and sanitation that they are classified by the kind of supply and sanitation available (12).   One of the most important water and environmental contaminants is human faeces, through which a variety of infectious diseases are spread.   Those include cholera, typhoid, infectious hepatitis and the bacterial and viral agents implicated in diarrhoeal diseases and intestinal parasites.   Because of the relative ease and low cost of intestinal parasite identification in human faeces, it has often been used as an index of environmental contamination.

In this study, 195 stool samples obtained from children under 3 years old - or 88% of the total number of children - were examined.   There was an overall rate of intestinal parasite infestation of 32%.   Twenty-six per cent of the children were found to harbour Giardia lamblia, 3% Entamoeba histolytica, 3% Hymenelopus nana, 3% Entamoeba coli and 1% Ascaris lumbercoides in their stools.   Twenty-nine per cent of the total were infested with one parasite and 3% were infested with two.   There were no cases with more than two infestations.   Thus, for all practical purposes, the principal potential offending agent found in the stools of these children, and the probably most prevalent parasite, was Giardia lamblia.

Giardia lamblia is an intestinal flagellate protozoan (unicellular) that usually lives in the small intestines.   It is transmitted in the form of cysts voided with faeces.   Infections are commonly asymptomatic, but gastrointestinal symptoms, both mild and severe, can occur.   Those include diarrhoea, abdominal pain, weight loss and malaise.   It usually runs a course of several weeks, but more severe, prolonged and chronic infections have been known.   Malabsorption is commonly associated with giardiasis and with protein-energy malnutrition.   It has been suggested that bacteria, Giardia and malnutrition operate synergistically to give enhanced pathogenicity, but no mechanism has yet been proposed (13).

Although an important question, the relation between giardiasis and the presence of symptoms and malnutrition cannot be elaborated here since, other than anthropometric measurements and stool analysis, the children were not subjected to clinical examinations or measurements. What the level of parasites in the stool indicates is the presence of an expected environmental contamination problem that may be contributing to the ill health of the members of these communities. Specifically, laboratory analysis revealed the presence of mostly Giardia lamblia, as opposed to other types of parasites, and in contrast to other regions of the West Bank. In the Hebron district, for instance, ascariasis is thought to be the predominant intestinal parasitic infestation (14). This information, however, still needs to be conclusively ascertained, for it relies primarily on clinical experience and not on a controlled investigation. It could be argued that the impressions regarding ascariasis prevalence in other districts are due to the ease of its identification and the relative difficulty of intestinal protozoa identification in general. Nevertheless, the knowledge of the presence of Giardia lamblia in this region as contracted with ascariasis in Hebron should make us cautious about dealing with disease in the West Bank as though it were homogeneous.

Significant association was found between parasitic infestation and increasing age of children in these villages (Table 7.5). This relationship between parasitic infestation and age has been found elsewhere, for instance in Pakistan. In that study, the 5-9-year-olds were found to have the highest rate of infestation (15). It is therefore likely that older children in the West Bank are also more infected. There was no significant relationship between parasitic infestation and the sex of the child, although males have a slightly higher rate of parasitic infestation than females, with 33% and 28% respectively. The environment, obviously, does not discriminate between boys and girls in terms of infestation.

TABLE 7.5

PARASITIC INFESTATION BY AGE
CHILDREN UNDER THE AGE OF THREE YEARS ONLY

Age	No. of parasites in the stool	One or more parasites in the stool	Total
	----------------percentages----------------------		
0-5 months	90	10	100
6-11 months	82	18	100
12-23 months	66	34	100
24-35 months	55	45	100

Total children: 195
Chi square: 14.183   p = 0.005

Wealth levels were also found to be determinants of parasitic infestation rates; 18% of the high, 31% of the middle and 49% of the low income group children had one or more parasites in their stools (Chi square 6.836; p = 0.05).   There was a strong association between crowding in the home and parasitic infestation.   Children who lived in more crowded dwellings had higher rates of parasitic infestation (Table 7.6).   Other than for crowding, there was no relationship between parasitic infestation and such dwelling features as water source or the presence or absence of latrines and other facilities.

TABLE 7.6

PARASITIC INFESTATION BY CROWDING IN HOUSEHOLDS
CHILDREN UNDER THE AGE OF THREE YEARS ONLY

Degree of crowding	No. of parasites in the stool	One or more parasites in the stool	Total
	---------------percentages---------------		
2 persons or less per room	77	23	100
3-4 persons per room	66	34	100
More than 4 persons per room	47	53	100

Total children: 195
Chi square: 10.78   p = 0.005

Nor was there any relationship between parasitic infestation and age, education or health behaviour of mother, such as drinking-water coverage.   These findings suggest that a generalised contamination of the environment rather than specific household sanitary conditions may be responsible for the presence of parasites in children's stools.

Parasitic diseases are known to be the diseases of poverty (16). Those who are at risk are usually individuals, communities or countries that cannot afford the costs of treatment and, more importantly, prevention in the form of a sanitary environment. Yet conventional health education efforts have traditionally been directed at changing individual behaviour (17), as if behaviour were not shaped and reinforced by the general social conditions under which individuals live.   Although the encouragement of sanitary behaviour may be of value under certain conditions, an attempt to change individual behaviour when the material and social conditions do not allow for such a change remains at best of limited value and at worst a useless expenditure of effort and financial resources.   In the Palestinian villages, along with the households' ability to afford proper sanitary facilities, water is the crucial variable that can determine whether or not health education efforts succeed.   Without an adequate supply of water, the maintenance of latrines, households and children in sanitary condition is difficult, and sometimes impossible.   Thus, although health education may impart an awareness of the need to keep the environment clean so as to avoid disease, this awareness remains useless without water.

Incidence of Diarrhoea

Reported incidence of diarrhoea, defined as a child having more than three liquid stools daily, within the two-week period immediately preceding the interviews yielded similar results to those obtained for parasitic infestation and nutritional status. Of a total of 219 children, 32% were reported as having had one or more episodes of diarrhoea within the two-week period. There was a strong association between reported diarrhoea episodes and the age of children; episodes tended to increase with increasing age up until the age of 23 months (Table 7.7).

TABLE 7.7

REPORTED DIARRHOEA INCIDENCE BY AGE OF CHILDREN
CHILDREN UNDER THE AGE OF THREE YEARS ONLY

		Reported Episodes	
Age	None	One or more	Total
		----percentages----	
0-5 months	74	26	100
6-11 months	58	42	100
12-23 months	59	41	100
24-35 months	85	15	100

Total children: 219
Chi square: 13.75   p = 0.005

No clear association was found between diarrhoea episodes and the sex of the child, although males had a slightly higher rate of diarrhoea episodes (35% for the males and 28% for females). Diarrhoea episodes were associated with wealth status; 14% of the high, 34% of the middle, and 39% of the low income children had one or more episodes of diarrhoea within the two weeks that preceded the survey. There were no significant relationships established between diarrhoea episodes and behavioural and feeding variables, even though it appeared that those who were given foods other than milk earlier (given Cerelac as weaning food and completely weaned earlier) tended to have higher rates of diarrhoea episodes (Appendix 11). Mothers' age and education did not have an impact on diarrhoeal disease among their children. In general, although they had some effect, behavioural and individual characteristics did not seem to influence the incidence of diarrhoeal diseases. Environmental conditions were more important. The presence or absence of refrigerators in dwellings appeared to determine, to some extent, the incidence of diarrhoeal diseases. Twenty-four per cent of those children who had refrigerators in their dwellings were reported as having had diarrhoea; 38% of those that did not have them suffered from the disease.   The proper storage of milk foods, away from possible sources of contamination, and in a temperature that does not encourage the proliferation of microorganisms may help to prevent diarrhoeal diseases.   This may be especially relevant in the storage of leftover infant foods.   The presence or absence of a piped water supply in the dwelling did not seem to affect diarrhoeal disease incidence, suggesting possibly a generalised contamination of the environment as opposed to the immediate living areas.   Internal latrines in dwellings seemed to influence the incidence of diarrhoeal diseases in the same unexpected way in which it influenced nutritional status.   Among those children who had internal latrines in their dwellings, 37% had diarrhoea. Among those who either had external latrines or none at all, 31% suffered from the disease.   Once again, although these findings are tentative, they raise the question whether internal latrines may facilitate the spread of disease, in situations where their sanitary maintenance is difficult.

In summary, then, of a total of 222 children under 3 years old in these three communities, 41% were found to be malnourished, based on a weight/length/age index; 32% were found to be infested with one or more intestinal parasites, mostly Giardia lamblia; and 32% were reported as having had one or more episodes of diarrhoea within the two weeks that preceded the survey.   Of a variety of possible socio-economic, behavioural and environmental deter-minants, wealth was found to consistently and positively affect health status; increasing wealth was associated with decreasing malnutrition, parasite infestation and diarrhoeal disease episodes.   Gender was found to be another determinant of nutritional status; female children were found to be significant-ly more malnourished than male children at all ages.   Although parasitic infestation and diarrhoeal disease episodes were found to be slightly higher among male than female children, with male/female ratios of 1.18 and 1.25 for parasitic and diarrhoeal diseases respectively, these ratios still appear to be in favour of males.   For males are known to be more susceptible to disease in general than females.   Genetic factors are involved here; sex differences in health and disease are influenced by the effects of the genes that are carried by the X chromosome and that influence the operation of the immune system.   Since females have a pair of these X chromosomes and males have only one, the presence of the pair in females is thought to contribute to the greater resistance to infection they experience (18).   Differ-ences in the rates of infection between males and females in infancy and childhood have been known to reach a male/female ratio of two or even three to one among newborns in more serious infections.   Moreover, the underreporting of diarrhoea episodes for female children cannot be ruled out, since mothers tended to be more attentive to the health of their male than their female children.

Environment was found to have an important influence on the children's health.   Water, latrines and refrigerators appeared to be to varying degrees the key influences, as opposed to other

factors that deal with behaviour more directly. The presence of
these facilities, in turn, was determined to a significant extent
by both the wealth status of the child's family and the educational level of the child's mother. Behavioural data yielded
vague and contradictory results. There was no clear association
between reported feeding and weaning patterns, sanitary habits,
post-natal follow-up of children and their health status, even
though slight tendencies in the evidence raised the possibility
that sanitary behaviour and medical follow-up of children could
be of some value. Some of the vagueness of the data was found to
result from the contradictory effects of education on the
behaviour of the mother.

But the method of data collection was found to be a fundamental
problem. Reported behaviour was contradicted by the evidence of
observation, leading us to conclude that respondents sometimes
did not tell us and sometimes did not know how they were actually
behaving. Physical, material and socio-economic conditions were
thought to place important constraints on the respondents'
ability to translate knowledge into action. Moreover, women
reported their health behaviour under the influence of two kinds
of biases: the first pushed them to respond as they thought we
wanted them to, or as they thought was proper (for example, to
say that they fed their children meat or eggs); the second bias
related to unconscious oblique behaviour patterns (for example,
unknowingly favouring boys over girls). These factors worked
together to yield unintelligible health behaviour data which, in
turn, failed to explain the observed health status assessment
results. This conclusion is further supported by the data
showing slightly higher incidence of parasitic infestation and
diarrhoeal episodes among boys than girls with opposite results
for nutritional status. Behavioural factors must have operated
to create the boys' nutritional status advantage.

The high infant and childhood mortality rates, in conjunction
with an evident problem of malnutrition and infection among
children, as indices for the population's overall health level,
indicate the general inadequacy of health levels in these
communities. As indices of the level of national development,
they indicate a problem of underdevelopment. As guidelines for
policymaking and planning, they indicate the need for improved
incomes, nutrition and environmental hygiene as the primary
solutions for these health problems. What the findings ultimately indicate is that, although the age of weaning may predispose
children to disease and illness, it is socio-economic and
political factors that eventually determine the actual disease
incidence and its outcome and the risk of dying. Thus, while
clinical medicine may be of substantial value to the people of
these communities under certain conditions, radical change in
their socio-economic and political conditions is required for the
solution of these health problems. Clinical and preventive
medicine can act as supports within this change but not the other
way around.

NOTES

1. Look at, for instance, Rubinstein, D, 'The Truth about West Bank Resistance', <u>Davar</u>, 5.2.85, English translation in <u>Israel Mirror</u>, no. 719, 8.2.85.

2. Landrigan, P J & Miller, B, <u>Epidemic of Acute Illness in the West·Bank</u>, unpublished report, Center for Disease Control, Atlanta, 1983, p. 14.

3. Mclaren & Read, op cit.

4. Ibid, p. 2.

5. Abolgassem, D et al, 'Assessment of the Nutritional Status of Pre-School Children in Mahabad Rural Areas', <u>Journal of Tropical Pediatrics</u>, Vol 29, 1983, pp. 329-332.

6. Look at, for instance, Winikoff & Brown, op cit; Berg, A, <u>The Nutrition Factor: Its Role in National Development</u>, Brooking Institute, Washington DC, 1973; Schoefield, S, <u>Development and the Problems of Village Nutrition</u>, Croom Helm, London, 1979; Mata, L, <u>The Children of Santa Maria Cauqe: A Prospective Field Study of Health and Growth</u>, MIT Press, Cambridge, MA, 1978.

7. Look at, for instance, Ebrahim, G J, <u>Paediatric Practice in Developing Countries</u>, Macmillan, London, 1981, pp. 58-60; Grosse, op cit, pp. 103-104; Mata, op cit, pp. 159-166.

8. Ebrahim, G J, <u>Child Health in a Changing Environment</u>, op cit, pp. 58-61; Popkin, B & Lim-Ybanez, M, 'Nutrition and School Achievement', <u>Social Science and Medicine</u>, Vol 16, 1982, pp. 53-61.

9. Shear-Wood, C, 'Early Childhood: The Critical Stage in Human Interactions with Disease and Culture', <u>Social Science and Medicine</u>, Vol 17, no 2, 1983, pp. 79-85.

10. Manderson, op cit; Laderman, C, 'Food Ideology and Eating Behaviour: Contributions from Malay Studies', <u>Social Science and Medicine</u>, Vol 19, no 5, 1984, pp. 547-559.

11. Look at, for instance, Isliker, H & Schurch, B, <u>The Impact of Malnutrition on Immune Defense in Parasitic Infestation</u>, Hans Huber, Bern, Switzerland, 1981.

12. Feachem, R, et al (eds), <u>Water Wastes and Health in Hot Climates</u>, John Wiley, Chichester, 1977; Mara, D & Feachem, R, 'Technical and Public Health Aspects of Low Cost Sanitation Programmes Planning', <u>Journal of Tropical Medicine and Hygiene</u>, Vol 83, 1980, pp. 229-240.

13. Isliker & Schurch, op cit, pp. 165-167.

14. This information was obtained through discussions with some physicians and laboratory technologists who work in the Hebron District.

15. Riaz, A P & Shahid, I R, 'Incidence of Intestinal Protozoan Parasites of Man in the Twin Cities of Rawalpindi-Islamabad', Journal of Pakistani Medical Association, July 1983, pp. 156-161.

16. Rosenfield, P, Golladar, F & Davidson, R K, 'The Economics of Parasitic Diseases: Research Priorities', Social Science and Medicine, Vol 19, no 10, 1984, pp. 1117-1126.

17. Brown, & Margo, 'Health Education', op cit, pp. 8-10.

18. Look at, for instance, Chojnacka, H & Abegbola, O K, 'The Determinants of Infant and Child Morbidity in Lagos, Nigeria', Social Science and Medicine, Vol 19, no 8, 1984, p. 804; Washburn, T & Medearis, D, 'Sex Differences in Susceptibility to Infection', Pediatrics, January 1965, pp. 59-62.

CHAPTER EIGHT

COMPETING MEDICAL SYSTEMS OR SYNTHESIS?

It is generally acknowledged that the major causes of illness in developing countries are infection and malnutrition (1). While in industrialised countries major causes of morbidity and death include cancer and circulatory diseases, in developing countries infections alone account for almost half of deaths. About two thirds of pre-school children suffer from malnutrition (2). Equally acknowledged is that these diseases are caused primarily by inadequate living conditions and that they are more amenable to prevention through improvements in living standards than to the administration of clinical cures.

The dearth of information regarding disease distribution in the occupied territories and the problems associated with inaccurate and incomplete reporting render attempts to delineate morbidity patterns difficult, and time trends for morbidity patterns almost impossible. However, the available information does indicate that infection (gastrointestinal in the summer and respiratory in winter) and malnutrition constitute major causes of morbidity and mortality in the region (3), and produce a morbidity picture not very dissimilar to that of many underdeveloped countries. What no one has examined so far are the changes in morbidity patterns that may have accompanied changes in the socio-economic environment. Differing food consumption patterns, changes in lifestyle and the advent of modern medicine may all have contributed to changes in disease and illness behaviour patterns. Members of the Union of Palestinian Medical Relief Committees, for example, note a tendency towards the rise of a mixed pattern of disease; such modern diseases as hypertension and diabetes are on the rise, while the diseases of underdevelopment persist (4).

As the physical examination of the population was not attempted, a comprehensive disease distribution picture cannot be obtained from the data on the three villages, but information obtained regarding incidence of reported illnesses does provide some interesting patterns, and possibly some insights. Of a total of 846 persons or 84% of the population, 11% reported one or more illnesses in autumn, 10% in winter and spring each, and 11% in the summer during the two weeks immediately preceding each inquiry (Table 8.1).

TABLE 8.1

INCIDENCE OF REPORTED ILLNESSES DURING THE TWO WEEKS
IMMEDIATELY PRECEDING VISITS BY SEASON

Diseases	Season/Month			
	September %	December %	March %	June %
One disease	8	8	8	10
Two diseases	2	2	2	22
Three diseases	1	0.5	0	0
Total, one or more diseases	11	10	10	11
Total persons sick	N	N	N	N
	196	186	189	210

Total population: 1846
Total households: 244

The rates of reported illnesses appeared to be higher among
adults than children. Among those over 14 years old, 22% were
reported as having had at least one illness throughout the four
seasons and within the two weeks that preceded each visit. In
contrast, 4% of the 3-14-year-olds and 8% of the 0-1-year-olds
were reported ill during those periods. Although the difference
between adults and children may actually reflect health and
disease status, it may also be due to the underreporting of
illness episodes among children. Mothers may be more likely to
omit reporting a child's illness because the child lacks adequate
mechanisms for self-expression.

A classification of the rates of reported illnesses by sex
indicated more episodes of illness among males than females; 17%
of the males and 10% of the females were sick at least once
during the follow-up period. This finding contrasts with other
findings, where survey data generally indicates higher rates for
women than for men for acute conditions, days of restricted
activity due to illness and doctor visits (5). The usual
discrepancy between the sexes has been variously explained. One
hypothesis is that traditional female excess in reported
morbidity is due to females having more "flexible role obligations" than males, which makes it easier for females to adopt the
sick role (6), resulting in biased estimates of sex differences
in morbidity (7). A second hypothesis is that role obligations
may play a larger role in determining when to relinquish the sick
role rather than its adoption (8). Third, it has been argued
that morbidity may be underestimated for men relative to women
due to more frequent proxy reporting for men in morbidity
surveys, and that certain causes of illness with a substantial
male excess make relatively greater contributions to total death
rates, while on the other hand, some other causes of illness with
a smaller male excess or a female excess make greater contribution to morbidity rates (9).

In the case of the three villages the discrepancy between the
sexes is reversed. This can also be variously explained. First,
men may tend to be sick more often than women and with more
serious episodes due to more difficult and unhealthy work
conditions. Second, such causes of illness as rheumatic and
arthritic diseases which have a smaller male excess or a female
excess and which make greater contributions to morbidity rates
elsewhere are not perceived as illnesses in these communities.
This perception would explain the discrepancy in reports between
this and other similar surveys. Third, given that illness
reports were obtained from women for the entire family, and given
the elevated status afforded to men in Palestinian society, a
reporting bias in favour of those regarded as important, the men
in the family, reflects itself as higher disease incidence among
males. A socio-cultural factor could thus account for the
difference. Lastly, the females' greater, X-chromosome-linked
resistance to infection may also account for the higher incidence
of disease among males than females, especially given that over
half the reported illnesses were infectious (Table 8.2).

TABLE 8.2

INCIDENCE OF REPORTED ILLNESS BY TYPE AND SEASON

Type of Illness	Season/Month-Percentages			
	September	December	March	June
Respiratory infection	18	29	30	22
Gastrointestinal	20	14	15	21
Eye	5	2	2	5
Skin	6	5	6	6
Reproductive Organ	7	5	6	6
Chronic	7	4	4	7
Other	37	41	37	33
Total Sick	N=196	N=186	N=189	N=210

Total Population: 1846

Table 8.2 indicates that almost half of the reported illnesses in
all four seasons were infectious. Respiratory and gastrointestinal diseases were the most common; respiratory infections
increased during winter and spring and gastrointestinal infections (mostly gastroenteritis and diarrhoea) increased in summer
and autumn. Eye diseases, again, mostly infectious, appeared to
be more prevalent during summer and autumn than at other times of
the year. The incidence of illness due to such chronic diseases
as hypertension, diabetes, heart disease and rheumatic and
arthritic diseases appeared to be low, with incidence not
exceeding 7% in any of the seasons. Whether this rate adequately
represents the prevalence of chronic diseases in these communities remains a question, especially since some of these
diseases, most notably hypertension, may go unnoticed for an
extended period because it frequently occurs without obvious
symptoms. The communities by and large did not seek medical care

regularly, usually only when specific problems occurred, and no automatic screening for such potential and hidden diseases as hypertension and diabetes exists in most West Bank medical establishments. None of the other illness categories questioned such as anaemia, a variety of bodily aches, fever of unknown origin, pregnancy problems, accidents and dental problems were presented as serious complaints by respondents. They together formed 33-41% of the total number of reported illnesses.

To the extent that respondents perceived illnesses as such, they indicated that infection was their main health problem. As elsewhere in the underdeveloped world, gastrointestinal diseases in the summer and respiratory infections in the winter constitute the major health complaints in these communities. The problem of suspected reporting bias, however, leaves such questions as disease incidence by age and sex unresolved. Other methods of measuring morbidity are also problematic. One of those measures, medically evaluated morbidity obtained from clinical medical records, such as the Birzeit clinic for instance, was not the preferred method for several reasons. Clinic records represent a rather biased sample; they contain information pertaining only to those who sought care at the clinic and not those who sought care elsewhere or used methods other than modern medical facilities to treat their diseases, or did not seek care. The inhabitants of these communities sought modern medical care in both Birzeit and Ramallah. It would thus have been impossible to make general statements based on data obtained in this way. Clinic records, moreover, could not explain how people respond to disease, nor the variety of ways in which they proceed to obtain cure. All the records could indicate was what the doctor did, not what the patient did with the doctor's orders, nor what other methods of cure that may have been used simultaneously. Added to these problems, the inaccurate and incomplete recording that predominates in medical institutions in general in the area renders medical records, if found, of limited use for research purposes. Short of extensive and very costly medical examinations, incidence of reported illnesses was found to be the most reasonable method of delineating the general disease picture in these communities.

Of all the tested possible morbidity determinants, both physical/sanitary and socio-economic, the two which correlated with reported illness were wealth and a piped water supply. Six per cent of the upper income group were found to have reported at least one illness during the course of the four follow-ups, while 13% of the middle income and 17% of the low income groups reported at least one illness. Of the environmental determinants water was most important; 7% of those who had internal piped water in their dwellings and 14% of those who either had no piped water at all or had running water external to their dwelling reported at least one illness during the course of the follow-up period. Thus, increased wealth and access to a piped water supply in dwellings were found to have an impact on decreasing the incidence of reported illnesses. These results are similar to those obtained for other underdeveloped countries. In the

Khartoum/Omdurman urban complex of Sudan, for instance, utilising similar methods of data collection, it was found that there was a sharp correlation between selected infectious diseases and the quality of the urban environment. It was also found that there were very large differences among the different type of residential areas; the gap between rich and poor was found to be no less acute in terms of vulnerability to disease than other criteria of social well-being (10).

Throughout the follow-up year, a total of 238 or 13% of the population were sick at least once during the two-week period immediately preceding the visits. On the whole, those who were sick tended to be repeatedly sick throughout the year. Vulnerability to disease in these communities appeared to be attached to particular individuals and to persist with these individuals throughout the year. Disease among these individuals was associated with wealth status and with the nature of water facilities at home. These findings support the view that vulnerability to disease is not uniform and tends to affect specific groups more than others. Vulnerability to disease is then class dependent to a significant extent, even in an underdeveloped country and at the village level.

Cross-tabulations of data on the educational level of women with incidence of reported illnesses in their families yielded somewhat confusing results. Fourteen per cent of those whose households had married women with no education at all reported at least one episode of illness in one of the follow-ups; while 8% of those who had married women with 1-5 years of schooling in their households reported one or more diseases during this period. But 11% of those whose households had women with 6 or more years of schooling reported at least one disease. Thus, up until the educational level of 5 school years, it appeared that increased education tended to be related to decreased illness incidence. The pattern, however, changes with further increases in education. This could be explained in terms of the possibly different view of disease of those women with 6 or more years of schooling. It could be argued that the higher educational level of those women, coupled with their comfortable material conditions relative to others, induces a change in consciousness from attention to basic needs to higher expectations in general, and more attention to health problems in particular. Because of this consciousness difference, they may actually tend to be more complete and particular in reporting illness incidence among their family members than the others. By providing relatively more accurate data they may, in effect, reduce the reported disparity between rich and poor households in terms of amount of disease. In other words, the observed differences in incidence of illness between rich and poor are probably an underestimation of the actual differences.

The Indigenous Medical System

The study of folk illnesses and indigenous medical systems in
Third World countries has traditionally been the domain of
medical anthropologists. Mainstream medical anthropology has
focused on cultural conflict; i.e., on the impact of the invasion
of Western scientific medicine on the indigenous medical system
and the manner in which local people respond to these changes.
Emphasis is placed on the notion of displacement of an old system
with a new one, or alternatively, on the survival of indigenous
forms of health care despite the strength and pervasiveness of
Western scientific medicine (12).

Anthropological studies of health systems in the Middle East are
not numerous, but one attempt at critically analysing the
dominant theoretical orientation of some of these studies has
been that of Soheir Morsy (13). She begins by noting the
contrast between indigenous conceptions of illness and biomedical
interpretations of disease:

> Unlike the biomedical dualistic orientation which
> differentiates "physical" and "mental" illness, the
> indigenous Middle Eastern integrated view of sickness
> is characterised by a holistic orientation. According-
> ly, all forms of illness are viewed as affecting the
> physical self, the patient's attitudes and moods, as
> well as his/her social relations. Sickness is regarded
> as both psychosocial and physical maladaption (14).

Morsy paints an idealistic image of the indigenous Middle Eastern
medical system; she treats it as though it were one system
practised with uniformity all over the Middle East. She asserts
that all forms of illness are viewed as coming from multiple
physical and psychological causes. In short, she treats the
Middle East as monolithic for the purpose of her argument,
obliterates variations and fails to take into account the
existence of a variety of indigenous medical systems - all with a
similar outlook, perhaps, but nonetheless different because of
the relatively wide cultural and other contextual differences
among Arab countries.

Despite this not-so-realistic view, however, her elaboration of
theoretical inadequacies found in the literature on the Middle
East and of their consequences on the understanding of Middle
East health systems is revealing. She points to the reductionist
and dualistic ideology which permeates Western medicine as the
reason why explanations of illness are reduced to a single cause.
She delineates the limitations of the analytical boundaries of
stressful roles and their relation to disease by noting the
failure to explain why some roles are more stressful than others,
and the way in which these roles are maintained by structural
elements. She maintains that the attention given to healing
leaves one under the impression that healing forms derive
straightforwardly from medical beliefs when in fact perfect
correspondence between them is absent. She stresses the need to

recognise the relation of beliefs to social conditions. In the end, she advocates an analysis that takes into consideration elements other than the family and the community, one that takes into account class and international relations and their effects on health, access to medical care, and the development of national health care policies. Her critique is relevant to medical anthropological studies of other cultures as well, to the extent that they focus primarily on the individual and on behaviour with little emphasis on the political and economic relations of the larger context and their effects on health and healing.

As is the case with other Third World countries (15), Western scientific medicine took root in its institutional form in Palestine with the penetration of British colonialism into the area and with Palestine's incorporation into the world economic system in the early twentieth century (16). Since then, the indigenous medical system has been subjected to a variety of modifications as a result of the changes in economic and social relations accompanying British colonialism. Over the years, and with the increasing use of money, markets and exchange, the response of the population to health and disease began to change; health and medical care underwent a gradual process of com-moditisation. As Cynthia Myntti has noted for North Yemen (17), social and economic transformations over the past 50 years or so were manifested in attitudinal change, away from the health-promoting behaviour that formed one of the foundations of the indigenous medical/belief system, to one that is based mostly, but not solely, on the purchase of a cure. This is not to say that the population did not benefit from Western scientific medicine and all the technology that accompanied it. Clearly, technologies such as immunisation, for instance, must have con-tributed to the sharp decline in morbidity and mortality during the British Mandate, along with the effects of the general improvement in the standard of living (18). Nor does it mean to say that the indigenous system was completely overcome and replaced by the new one; it persists until today but in a modified form that appears to have adapted new realities to old concepts. The Western scientific medical system has gradually taken a dominant position, yet folk illnesses persist, and indigenous cures continue to be sought especially by the rural population.

The indigenous medical system in the three villages is based on classical Arabic medicine as well as a mixture of other practices that seem to have incorporated the experience of social transfor-mations that have accompanied changing times. Means of healing can roughly be divided into four categories. Practitioners of them have been handed down the gifts of al-Tib al-Arabi (Arabic medicine) from their ancestors. Physical means of healing include tajbir (bonesetting), kawi (cautery), takhrim (pricking with a needle), kassat hawa (cupping) and tamlis (massage). Herbal means include both the ingestion and the external use of some 70 locally available herbs and plants. Some of those are known to contain physiologically active compounds, whose therapeutic value is well established by Western scientific medical standards. Those include yansoun (Pimpinella anisum), mayramieh (Saliva triloda), and ja'deh (teucrium polium) among many others that are known to elicit a therapeutic response (19).

Dietary means are used for healing as well as prevention of disease. Cold or light foods are used in general to help a patient through an illness and special diets are prescribed for specific ailments. Those include rice water for gastrointestinal disease, removal of milk from the diet for flatulence and diarrhoea (20), and barley and parsley water for the treatment of urinary tract disease. Spiritual means are many and include the use of al-ein al-zarka (the blue eye), al-kaf (the palm) and al-hijab (the amulet, which could be a verse from the Qur'an) or 'admet-al-jozeh (a wolf's throat piece) among other things. These are usually especially prepared for the patient by al-sheikh (the spiritual healer). Special prayers over the ill person utilising herbs and other materials for burning are also commonly used to drive the evil eye, that is, the cause of the disease, away from the patient. The same rationale or underlying principle applies to the use of most other spiritual means of healing: the intention is to drive the evil eye or spirit out of the sick person.

In these communities, the etiology of disease is perceived as being multiple. A mixture of modern explanations and older forms is usually used to describe the process of becoming sick. Hypertension, according to our informants, is brought about by a constellation of forces. Age is one of these factors; but it only predisposes to disease and does not necessarily cause it. Ultimately, it is al-ghadab (anger) or al-za'al (emotional upset) that precipitates the disease and not age or other biological processes. Al-za'al underlies the explanation offered for many of the diseases, especially among those who are older, and the al-za'al-disease relationship is used to keep the younger "rebellious" generation under control. Heart disease is due to an unbalanced diet, to al-za'al and to old age. But it can also be precipitated by ein-al-hassoud (the envy of the evil eye). Diarrhoea and other diseases of childhood are often interpreted in terms of envy - especially in the cases of male children and blue-eyed, fair-haired female children (who are especially valued by society) - although other mechanisms for disease, such as exposure to the cold and to air currents are simultaneously offered as explanations. Childhood deaths are thought to be due to a variety of causes: exposure to cold, especially when the child is wet or immediately after bathing when the body is warm; to diarrhoea; and also to the influence of the spirits. A specific spirit, tabi'at al-niswan (the women's follower), is thought to exert both helpful and harmful influences. Harm includes the death of newly born male children. To treat this problem, some of the inhabitants of these communities have sought the Samaritans of the Nablus hills, who are known to be experts in the treatment of tabi'a problems. On the whole, then, the occurrence of disease in these communities is explained at least partially in social-relational terms.

Preventive health behaviour is still part of these villages, even though changes in the larger context have had their impact in modifying or rendering obsolete some local preventive practices. If a local <u>dayya</u> delivers a child, for example, she applies <u>kuhl</u> to the ridge of the eyelids so as to prevent the occurrence of eye disease.

People in general avoid exposure to the cold or to air currents when the body is hot, and especially after a bath and when the hair is wet. Eating eggs in the evening is avoided so as not to precipitate stomach problems. Eggs and fish are rarely mixed in the course of a meal for the same reason. A variety of gadgets and amulets are attached to the bodies and bedding, especially of children, to prevent the evil effects of the envious eye. In short, though many of the preventive practices that are the product of the old belief system are no longer viable, others that appear not to come into conflict with modern methods have persisted. And as the data on responses to disease indicates (Table 8.3), old methods are used, along with the new ones in such a way as to suggest synthesis rather than competition, and adaptation of beliefs and practices to new realities.

TABLE 8.3

RESPONSE TO/TREATMENT OF ILLNESS BY SEASON

Treatment Type	Those with at least one reported illness within the two weeks preceding visits			
	September %	December %	March %	June %
Doctor	39	27	35	47
Drugs without doctor's orders	20	44	38	28
<u>Dayya</u>	4	5	13	7
Herbs	20	34	23	12
Physical means (indigenous)	14	20	16	11
Spiritual means	1	3	3	2
Dietary manipulation	7	3	3	2
Did nothing	12	10	11	18
	<u>N</u>	<u>N</u>	<u>N</u>	<u>N</u>
Total sick	196	186	189	210
Total population	1846	1846	1846	1846

* Totals do not add to 100 per cent since more than one course of action was taken to treat episodes of illness.

Although the various local medical practices relied on different instruments and methods, the physical and spiritual means of healing utilised seemed to share common principles and charac-teristics with traditional medical practices of other Arab countries, such as North Yemen (14). But as is the case with North Yemen, the popular base around which this tradition once

thrived was being eroded by the economic and social and, therefore, attitudinal changes that were taking place at the village
level.   The service of <u>dayyas</u> was hardly being sought, while
other practices, although still being utilised for healing, were
mostly appreciated by the older generation, and especially by
those who were illiterate. Yet despite this downward trend, some
aspects of the practice continue to thrive, as with the herbal
and dietary means of healing we observed.   These practices
persist substantially at the popular level, despite the tough
competition of drugs, injections and stethoscopes.

By far the most prevalent response to disease in these communities appears to be to seek Western scientific medical
treatment. Visiting a doctor or buying drugs without prescription were the methods most used to cure disease in all four
seasons (Table 8.3). Those were followed by the utilisation of
herbal and physical means of healing largely derived from the old
indigenous medical system, by dietary manipulation, and, lastly,
by the spiritual means. The spiritual means appear to be on the
way to extinction, for they had been relegated to minor importance for the treatment of illness by 1981. These findings do
not differ from those for other developing societies where, it is
believed, modern medicine in recent years has become the first
choice of most Third World peoples (22).

Table 8.3 also indicates that there was a tendency towards a
decreased number of visits to doctors during winter, with a
compensatory increase in the use of drugs without doctor's orders
as well as herbal and physical means of healing. This makes
total sense, given the severity of winter, the lack of transportation and the understanding of the contribution cold and wet
make to the development of disease. Indeed, the Birzeit clinic
also observes a sharp drop in its workload on rainy days.

The total figures for the four follow-ups yielded basically
similar results. Of 238 persons reported sick at least once, 67%
saw a doctor and bought drugs without prescription at least once,
53% used herbs, 37% used physical means, 20% visited a <u>dayya</u>, 11%
used dietary means, and 2% used spiritual means to treat their
illnesses at least once. Eight per cent did nothing at all. The
majority, or 83%, combined more than one method, mostly modern as
well as indigenous health care.   As many as 6 methods of
treatment were recorded as being used for one sickness alone, and
just 9% consistently used only modern methods during the course
of the four follow-ups. Far from being extinct, then, indigenous
medicine in these communities is still being sought and practiced, albeit in a modified form. Changes in the socio-economic
context appeared to have undermined the basis upon which the
spiritual means of healing stand; consequently, they were
relegated to a minor position. Other indigenous treatment
methods, however, survived and were incorporated into modern
conceptions of disease and its treatment, resulting in the
creation of the mixture of treatment noted.

Recent years have increasingly witnessed the decentralisation of traditional operations in the direction of self-medication.   In the past, indigenous medical specialists were the primary source of treatment and advice on how to handle the sick.   Specialties tended to be sex-specific: bonesetters and spiritual healers were largely men; cupping and other types of operations were performed by specialised women, often the <u>dayya</u> of the village; herbalists did include men, although in these villages herbs were largely the specialty of women.   The tricks of the trade were attached to individuals, who were sought for health and sickness care, just as doctors are sought today.   The intrusion of Western scientific medicine and the general social and economic changes of the recent years appear to have led to a shift towards decentralisa-tion and popularisation of practices.   The aging of the old specialists, the lack of interest of the younger generation in learning the indigenous methods and in maintaining the old specialist-centered system are contributing to the transformation of the indigenous medical system into a tradition of popular medicine practised by most people.   If this is true, then one would expect the survival of the indigenous medical practices at the level of individual practice and the disintegration of the old system of specialists in the future.

Cross-tabulation of responses to disease by wealth status for the four follow-ups revealed the expected results that increased wealth status was associated with increased visits to doctors and increased consumption of drugs without doctors' orders (Table 8.4).   Eighty-two per cent of those within the high income group visited the doctor at least once during the year, while 68% of the middle income group and 43% of the low income group visited a doctor during that period.   The same trend was observed for drug consumption, which was noted to increase with increasing wealth. The middle income group appeared to utilise the services of <u>dayyas</u> and physical means of healing more often than the other groups.   It is not exactly clear why this should occur, but it is possible that those who are poor tend to focus on the basic requirements of living to an extent that discourages them from seeking even the cheaper types of care available in their village.   The positive association between wealth status and the utilisation of modern scientific medicine in these communities supports similar findings elsewhere in Third World countries, which suggest that physicians and modern medicine are by far the first choice of people, when confronted with disease, if given the material ability to seek this type of care (23).   The concreteness and dramatic impact of modern Western medicine, for example, the effect of antibiotics in reducing fevers, make it by far the most preferred method.

TABLE 8.4

RESPONSE TO DISEASE BY WEALTH STATUS

Method of Treatment	Wealth Status*		
	High %	Medium %	Low %
Doctor	82	68	43
Dayya	9	22	14
Drugs without doctor's order	91	65	64
Herbs	55	51	57
Physical means	27	39	29
Spiritual means	0	11	2
Dietary manipulation	9	10	10
	N	N	N
Total in income category	181	1500	165

* Totals do not add to 100 per cent since more than one course of action was taken to treat illness.

The effect of education on the type of health care sought during sickness was also important (Table 8.5). A pattern of increasing visits to doctors in sickness was found with increasing educational levels of the married women of childbearing age within the sick person's household. A reverse pattern was observed for the utilisation of dayya services; persons with more educated women in their households tended to seek dayya services less. For all other responses - drugs, herbs, physical, spiritual and dietary means - increasing educational levels of married women in the sick persons' homes resulted in an increase in their use.

TABLE 8.5

RESPONSE TO DISEASE BY EDUCATIONAL LEVELS OF
MARRIED WOMEN OF CHILDBEARING AGE AT HOME

Method of Treatment	Educational Levels of Women in Years*		
	None %	1-5 %	6 or more %
Doctor	60	72	88
Dayya	22	18	9
Drugs without doctors' orders	60	68	97
Herbs	49	59	61
Physical means	35	41	45
Spiritual means	33	0	3
Dietary manipulation	8	9	21
	N	N	N
Total in education category	1281	269	295

* Totals do not add up to 100 per cent since more than one course of action was taken to treat illness.

Education, then, appears not only to increase the use of modern medical services and self-medication, as has been shown for other Third World countries (24), but also to increase the utilisation of all other services as well. It may be reasonable to suggest that education imparts its effects on the consciousness in such a way as to induce a greater awareness of the presence of disease and the need for appropriate action or actions.

In summary, then, morbidity data in these three communities suggests the persistence of a high rate of infectious diseases forming the bulk of the population's health problems. Incidence of reported illnesses was found to be associated with wealth status as well as the availability of piped water supply in households. Thus both poverty and inadequate environmental conditions appear to contribute to the occurrence of disease and point to the need for improved incomes and general living conditions. Data on responses to illnesses indicates that, given the absence of material constraints, Western scientific medicine in the form of both doctors and drugs is far the most preferred choice for health and sickness care. However, contrary to what may have been expected, the indigenous medical system was found to persist, but in a form that successfully adapted to new concepts of disease and new social realities. While some elements of the indigenous medical system were considerably undermined, other elements had been successfully incorporated into the new consciousness of health and disease. Both education and wealth were found to be contributory to the formation of this new consciousness and to the development of new ways in which healing could be achieved. As was the case with the emergencies of new sources of wealth, these communities appear to have been quick to seize upon the new medical care opportunities in such a way as to create a balance between health care needs and the socio-economic reality of individual families, the community and the larger context. The notion of competition between medical systems thus appears to be inadequate in that it can only allow for the examination of the interaction between indigenous and modern medical systems in terms of opposing polarity and contradictory logic. It is necessary to move outside its analytical boundaries for a more adequate explanation.

NOTES

1. See, for instance, Muir, Gray, & Fowler, op cit, pp. 206-208; Ebrahim, 1981, op cit; Schoefield, op cit.

2. Muir, Gray & Fowler, op cit, pp. 206-208; Ebrahim, 1981, op cit, p. 3; Schoefield, op cit, p. 11.

3. Katbeh, op cit; Puyet, J H, <u>Infant Mortality Studies Conducted among Selected Refugee Camp Communities in the Near East</u>, United Nations Relief and Works Agency, Vienna, 1979, p. 6; Tamari, & Giacaman, op cit, Part II, p. 17.

4. This information was obtained by the author from respresentative members of the Union of Palestinian Medical Relief Committees through discussion.

5. Waldron, I, 'Sex Differences in Illness', 1983, op cit, p. 1107.

6. Marcus, A, Seeman, T & Telesky, C, 'Sex Differences in Reports of Illness and Disability: A Further Test of the Fixed Role Hypothesis', <u>Social Science and Medicine</u>, Vol 17, no 15, 1983, p. 993.

7. Waldron, 'Sex Differences in Illness', op cit, p. 1118.

8. Marcus et al, op cit.

9. Waldron, 'Sex Differences in Mortality', op cit, p. 1108.

10. Herbert, D & Hijazi, N, 'Ill-Health and Health-Care in Kartoum/Omdurman', <u>Social Science and Medicine</u>, Vol 18, no 4, 1984, pp. 335-343.

11. Look at, for instance, Wylie, R, 'Effutu Curing: Preliminary Survey of Traditional and Spiritual Healers', <u>Current Anthropology</u>, vol 24, no 3, 1983, pp. 393-402; Faberga, H, 'On the Specificity of Folk Illnesses', <u>South Western Journal of Anthropology</u>, Vol 26, 1970, pp. 305-314; Suarez, M M, 'Etiology, Hunger and Folk Diseases in the Venezuelan Andes', <u>Journal of Anthropological Research</u>, Vol 30, 1974, pp. 41-54; Koo, L, 'The Use of Food to Treat and Prevent Disease in Chinese Culture', <u>Social Science and Medicine</u>, Vol 18, no 9, 1984, pp. 757-766.

12. Myntti, C, 'Changing Attitudes Towards Health: Some Observations from the Hujaria', in Pridham, B R (ed), <u>Economy, Society and Culture in Contemporary Yemen</u>, Croom Helm, Kent, 1985; Foster, G, 'Anthropological Research Perspectives on Health Problems in Developing Countries', <u>Social Science and Medicine</u>, Vol 18, no 10, 1984, pp. 847-8541; Davidson, J, 'The Survival of Traditional Medicine in a Peruvian Barriada', <u>Social Science and</u>

Medicine, Vol 17, no 17, 1983, pp. 1271-1280; Pederson, D & Coloma, C, 'Traditional Medicine in Ecuador: The Structure of the Non-Formal Health Systems', <u>Social Science and Medicine</u>, Vol 17, no 17, 1983, pp. 1249-1255; Abosede, O A, 'Self-Medication: An Important Aspect of Primary Health Care', <u>Social Science and Medicine</u>, Vol 19, no 7, 1984, pp. 699-703.

13. Morsy, S, 'Towards a Political Economy of Health: A Critical Note on the Medical Anthropology of the Middle East', <u>Social Science and Medicine</u>, Vol 15B, 1981, pp. 159-163.

14. Ibid, pp. 159-160.

15. See, for example, Paul, J, 'Medicine and Imperialism', in Ehrenreich, op cit, pp. 271-281; Fanon, F, 'Medicine and Colonialism', in ibid, pp. 229-251.

16. Owen, R (ed), op cit.

17. Myntti, in Pridham, op cit, p. 170.

18. Hill, op cit, p. 298.

19. For further information regarding the therapeutic use of botanical compounds, see, for instance, Chase et al, <u>Remington's Pharmaceutical Sciences</u>, 14th edition, Macmillan, Eaton, 1970; Istfan, F, <u>Materia Medica of the Organic Chemical Substances</u>, American University of Beirut Press, Beirut, 1934.

20. Some populations of the Mediterranean region are known to suffer from lactase deficiency especially in adulthood. Lactase is the enzyme of the small intestines that breaks down the milk sugar lactose in preparation for absorption. The enzyme deficiency can lead to malabsorption of lactose, which in turn can produce flatulence and diarrhoea. Thus the practice is not altogether unsound.

21. Myntti, C, <u>Health and Healing in Rural North Yemen</u>, unpublished document, Cairo, Egypt, 1985.

22. Foster, op cit, pp. 847-854.

23. Ibid, p. 847; Morsy, op cit, p. 161.

24. Abosede, op cit, pp. 699-703.

CHAPTER NINE

TOWARDS MORE APPROPRIATE HEALTH POLICIES AND PRACTICES

The findings of this study indicate that economic and social relations, specifically those of gender and class, are key determinants of health status in the three communities studied. They interact with and are reinforced by military occupation policies that render the possibilities for improvements in health status at best unlikely, unless the Palestinian response to the problems of ill health is changed. Specifically, we found that the infant mortality rate, as measured by an infant mortality index, was 91 deaths/1000 live births for the 10-year period preceding the survey, peaking at around 1977. As an indicator of the population's health status, this figure shows that the health picture in these communities is far from satisfactory. In addition, the data suggests that over the past 10-year period infant mortality has been on the decline; therefore, health levels have probably been improving. This trend is thought to be due to the improved incomes of these communities' inhabitants as a result of the opening-up of work opportunities in Israel and abroad on a scale that reduced unemployment to a minimum. These changes have taken place despite Israeli occupation policies and despite the general state of neglect of both the health services network and village needs in general. They remain temporary in nature, obtained at an unacceptable cost and subject to swift and damaging reversals, always depending on the needs and interests of the Israeli regime. Today, the indicators are that the trend in the inhabitants' health status may be reversing, as a reflection of the economic recession in the Gulf states and the economic crisis and skyrocketing inflation in Israel.

Although the age at first marriage of women in these communities is rising, and their educational levels are improving considerably, fertility levels remain high, with a total fertility of 8.67 and a birth rate of 43/1000. Poorer women were found to have a higher number of children under 3 years old, a finding which supports the notion that in these communities children are seen as economic and social security. The effects of wage labour, the increasing neglect of the land, the absence of a state welfare system and military occupation and general insecurity all favour a high birth rate as the only guarantee for the future. These appear to offset the effects of other, countervailing, fertility determinants.

Morbidity data on children under 3 years old reveal serious health problems similar to those of children in other Third World countries. Nutritional levels were found to be inadequate; 41% of these children were found malnourished. Diarrhoea is a major hazard to health; to the extent that 32% of the children were reported to have had at least one episode within the two weeks preceding interviews. The rate of parasitic disease infestation of 32% among the children points to environmental contamination as a health hazard and as the medium through which the interaction between malnutrition and infection which often leads to death may operate. Morbidity data for both adults and children also indicates that infections that are relatively easily preventable - mostly through improvements in the environment - are major causes of ill health in these communities.

By far, the most outstanding findings of this study are the associations between poverty, gender and ill health. The wealth status of households was found to significantly influence the majority of the health parameters studied, in addition to improving living and sanitary conditions of families. Those who were wealthy by village standards were found to be healthier and to have better living standards than those who were poor. Although such findings have been repeatedly documented for other societies, they nevertheless are significant. In the Palestinian context, such documentation is hard to find, and awareness of the extent of its significance, even at the village level, is not high. The relationship between health status and gender was found to be important as well. Mortality data suggest higher mortality among female than male children. The rate of malnutrition among female children was almost double that of males; female infants were found to be significantly more malnourished at all ages and to suffer from its more serious forms. Although a comparison of the remaining child morbidity data revealed similar results for both sexes, they nevertheless suggest preferential treatment of male children as male children's biological disadvantage was expected to yield higher morbidity rates for this group. Thus, between the effects of wealth on the standard of living, educational levels and health status and the effects of gender on health status, a picture of poor female children - at the bottom of the advantage scale and the top of the risk of disease one - emerges. On the whole, these findings suggest that a radical improvement in health status requires no less than a change in the nature of the division of labour, both within society, and between Palestinian society and the dominant Israeli society.

Lastly, although the survey method of studying community health was found useful and did contribute to the generation of a valuable health database, it was also found to have limitations. Surveys contribute to a description of phenomena frozen at one moment in time. This snapshot view of reality leaves one unable to understand the processes through which these phenomena develop, unless supported by other methods of investigation. In the case of this study, it was observation and a work relationship of several years with these communities that ultimately

provided the basis for a proper understanding of the processes of
health and disease.   In the end, the experience of this study
suggests that an interdisciplinary approach to the study of
community health can be of great value.

While the results of this study cannot be generalised to the
occupied territories at large, they do provide the foundation
upon which to raise questions regarding the dominant conceptions
of health in the area and the outlines of a preliminary appraisal
of health policies and practices under Israeli military rule.
Several issues of relevance to general West Bank health problems
can be identified, albeit tentatively.   First, doubts are raised
about the appropriateness of the biomedical framework as the all-
encompassing view of health and medical care, and about the
legitimacy of the policies and practices it determines.   The
health problems of the population of these three villages have
been shown to be rooted in social, economic and political
determinants.   Disease is to a significant extent a manifestation
of these phenomena.   A view which holds disease to be a function
of individual biological variables is thus simply inadequate; it
renders the task of properly understanding health and disease
impossible, and reduces medical and health practice to the
institution of temporary clinical cures.   Clinical cures cannot
solve the nutritional problems of children in these villages, nor
of rural children of the West Bank, where 70% of the population
live.   Even if healing is achieved at the clinical level, it can
only last as long as children are isolated from the social and
ecological environment that brings about malnutrition to begin
with.   The centralised and curative forms of health service
currently proliferating in the West Bank thus cannot provide a
lasting response to these health problems.   Meanwhile, they are
exhausting scarce financial resources.   Indeed, in the Palestinian context, where survival is to a large extent dependent on
the generation of funds externally, one cannot but fear a crash,
which would dissolve the mirage of economic well-being and turn
the curative centres and hopes for a healthy future into rubble.
I am not questioning the need for some hospitals and curative
centres in the area; they can clearly be of benefit.   The problem
is rather to formulate a health strategy that takes into
consideration the health needs and priorities of the majority as
well as the problem of limited resources, while keeping in mind
the Palestinians' need to be freed from economic dependence on
both Israel and the Arab world.

The second issue requiring attention arises from the mainstream
nationalist view of the causes of ill health in the occupied
territories.   The findings of this study suggest that the formula
"colonialism equals ill health" requires substantial modification.   Although Israel's occupation polices are in the long run
dangerous to the population's health, this is not always true in
the short term and in specific settings.   Colonial rule can have
the unintended effect of improving health status, despite a
noticeable deterioration in the health services infrastructure.
For what ultimately determines whether a population is healthy or
not is primarily the overall socio-economic setting within which

ill health develops: and only secondarily the provision of health services. These findings underline the need for a reformulated understanding of health, a reorganisation of priorities and a modification of practices so that they may truly contribute to the improvement of health status.

The inadequacies of the "colonialism equals ill health" formula go even further. The results of this study strongly suggest that ill health is also a function of inequalities existing in the society before the advent of military occupation. The problems of gender along with those of poverty, although interactive with occupation policies, are also endogenous. These problems will continue to place a heavy burden of disease on individuals and on the nation as a whole, even after liberation, precisely because their origins are also found in the inequitable nature of Palestinian social organisation. To continue placing the blame for these social ailments on occupation alone is to obscure reality in such a way as to ensure the perpetuation of this state of affairs for a very long time to come. It may well be that primacy should be afforded to the struggle for national libera- tion. But a neglect of issues of social justice at the internal level can only serve to reinforce the status quo and lay the grounds for an unhealthy Palestinian society in the future.

While the progressive initiative in health currently represents the only genuine effort to place the problem of ill health within the context of a social explanation, and as such remains a potentially major force for change, it nevertheless requires further development. Female children in these three villages were shown to be vulnerable to malnutrition, disease and death by virtue of their gender as well as of other causes. Since it is unlikely that other groups will be inclined to make special efforts to deal with the gender problem and its ill effects on health, the task becomes the responsibility of the women's movement. It is thus not sufficient to establish nursery schools and literacy programmes. The efforts needed require more far- reaching changes at the level of the larger structures. They require fundamental changes in the institutions and relations that bring about and perpetuate a debasement in the status of women in general, and the health problems encountered in these villages in particular.

Clearly, a range of political prerequisites are needed for the formulation of an alternative health strategy. Although a detailed elaboration of those is beyond the scope of this work, an outline of what may be required is in order. From the women's movement what is first needed is an analysis of the ways in which internal structures and processes bring about the subordination of women in Palestinian society, and of the way in which these forces interact with the external factors that subjugate women as well as the nation as a whole. With such analyses the movement would be able to address the specific problems of women and health under occupation. Also needed is the consolation of a united women's front that can demand change from the society at large, while at the same time attempting to meet the urgent need

of women. Women could struggle for legal equality, the right of
equal political representation and equal opportunities for
employment and education, among other issues. Precisely because
a state structure is still in the process of formation - given
that the Palestine Liberation Organisation represents to an
extent a government-in-exile - there is a need to press for such
demands at the present. The lesson learned from the Algerian
experience was that even a once-heralded women's movement - one
which entailed the active participation of women in the struggle
for liberation and raised the hopes for a radical transformation
in their general conditions - could be brought to a quick end in
the post-liberation stage. The real irony of the Algerian case
is that the women participated in bringing about their downfall.
This was signalled as early as at the First Congress of the
National Union of Algerian Women in 1966, where it was declared
that:

> The congress must ... entirely devote itself to the
> protection of the family unit ... through the es-
> tablishment of structures that conform to the Algerian
> personality and to Arab-Islamic culture (1).

From the political leadership, what is urgently needed is the
commitment to restore the struggle to its proper context and
dimensions, a commitment to the solution of health and development problems without destructive effects of factional politics
coming in the way of an adequate response to military occupation.
What is needed is a commitment to the principles of social
justice and the fulfillment of the needs of the majority based on
a well worked out list of priorities grounded in the health and
social realities. There is also a need for the allocation of
resources based on need and equity and not demand. For demand is
shaped least of all by the voices of those who need help most
- the invisible rural poor and women - but rather by those who
are politically and economically powerful and least in need.
Finally, what is needed are health strategies, policies and plans
that form part of a wider development strategy aimed at the
reduction of inequalities in Palestinian society while at the
same time striving for national liberation and economic and
social independence from the grips of others.

Several questions of relevance to health policy formation still
need to be resolved. These include the contradictory effects of
education on health and feeding behaviour. Is it possible to
stifle the possible ill effects of conventional education on the
feeding behaviour of mothers, for example, the increased use of
powdered milk to feed infants with increased educational levels?
Or is the apparent contradiction between the desire to appear
modern and healthy behaviour unresolvable? Is the increased use
of powdered milk a manifestation of conditions that necessitate
it, such as the increasing incorporation of women into the labour
market? If this is the case, should the problem be handled by
continuing to preach the use of breast milk despite the objective
constraints, or by accepting reality and attempting to provide
conditions that would allow for minimal health damage? The

increasing incorporation of Palestinian women into the wage labour market in the West Bank and Israel also needs to be studied. What are the characteristics of the sector of the female population most likely to move into wage labour? What are the rate and extent of their movement? What are the implications of this movement for family health and for the status of women in society? These are but some of the questions that need to be answered, at least in part, before appropriate policy formulations can be attempted.

NOTE

1.   M'rabet, F, 'La Femme Algérienne, Suivi de Les Algériennes',
      Paris, 1969, p. 108, quoted in Salman, M, 'Arab Women', in
      Rothschild, J (ed), <u>Forbidden Agendas: Intolerance and
      Defiance in the Middle East</u>, al-Saqi, London, 1984, p. 137.

APPENDIX ONE

GLOSSARY OF LOCAL ARABIC TERMS AND EXPRESSIONS

al-ein al-zarka
: the blue eye, thought to protect from envy

al-ghadab
: anger

al-hijab
: amulet

al-'ilm mal
: education is money

al-jizeh sutra
: marriage is protection

al-kaf
: the five-fingered palm, thought to protect from envy

al-za'al
: emotional upset

ajnabieh
: foreigner, denoting a female

atiet al-jorah
: a saying denoting the promise in marriage of a girl infant, literally meaning a gift from the pit of birth

baira
: leftover, on the shelf, a saying denoting a woman who has remained single and is not fit for marriage

dayya
: village midwife (as distinguished from one who is formally medically trained)

diwan
: a community centre that is collectively shared by members of the extended family for the purpose of family meetings, entertainment and the reception of guests

ein al-hasud
: the eye of the envious, thought to precipitate illness and catastrophes

gharibeh
: stranger, denoting a female

hamula
: extended family

hara
: street or village subsection, usually occupied by the members of one extended family

ibn al-halal
: literally meaning the son of plenty or the unforbidden son and denoting a suitable prospective husband

<u>ihna ma 'indnash banat bitishtghel</u>	we do not have girls who work
<u>kasat hawa</u>	air cups. A vacuum is created in the cup by lighting a fire inside it then it is applied to the back of patients as a method of treatment of a variety of illnesses.
<u>kawayeh</u>	cauterer, denoting a woman
<u>kuhl</u>	pulverized antimony potassium tartarate. It is applied to the eyelids of women for aesthetic reasons and the eyes of children to protect them against neonatal eye disease
<u>Kur'an</u>	the Muslim holy book
<u>leshka</u>	an Arabised version of a Hebrew word meaning bureau and denoting the Israeli Bureau of Employment responsible for registering Palestinian wage workers in Israel. The Arabic usage of the term now refers to the bureau truck that collects Palestinian workers from their villages. A <u>leshka</u> woman, therefore, is one who goes on the truck.
<u>mujabber</u>	bone setter, denoting a man
<u>mukhtar</u>	extended family head
<u>naksa</u>	literally meaning relapse, but used here as a euphemism for the 1967 Arab-Israeli war defeat
<u>nasib</u>	good luck or fortune, used here to denote a prospective suitor in marriage
<u>ni'meh</u>	blessing or gift from God
<u>sitti</u>	a title used to address an elderly woman or one who is of high status, literally meaning grandmother
<u>sheikh</u>	a term denoting a male leadership role (spiritual or other) literally meaning old man
<u>tabun</u>	local hand-made oven

tabi'at al-niswan   literally meaning the women's follower.
                            A spirit that oversees newly delivered
                            women and that can bring harm to newly
                            born children

taghieh   tyrant, denoting a woman

APPENDIX TWO

SURVEY QUESTIONNAIRES

Questionnaire 1: Information on household members

1. Name
2. Relation to head of household
3. Age
4. Sex
5. Marital status
6. Ability to read and write
7. Number of years of schooling
8. Number of years of technical training
9. Number of years of literacy training in adulthood
10. Number of years of university training
11. Primary occupation
12. Location of employment
13. Secondary employment
14. Location of employment

Questionnaire 2: Information on household

1. Total number of people living at home
2. Total number of rooms in the dwelling
3. Is there a kitchen in the dwelling?
4. Is there a latrine in the dwelling and what type (internal or external)?
5. Is there a bath area in the dwelling?
6. What is the dwelling's water source?
7. Is piped water available in the dwelling? Are there internal or external pipes?
8. How and where is water stored?
9. What is the source of drinking-water in this household?
10. Is electricity available in this household, and what is its source?
11. Do you heat your dwelling in winter, and what method of heating do you use?
12. How do you dispose of rubbish?
13. Do you own a radio, television, refrigerator, gas range, washing machine, car or other amenities?
14. What type of fuel do you use for cooking?
15. Do you own land? Is it arable? What is the total amount of land holdings of this household, and where is the land located?
16. What type of produce do you grow? Do you sell it or use it for family consumption or both?
17. Do you store food for household consumption during winter? What type? Where?
18. Do you own animals? What kind? Where do you keep them?

19. Do you use animal manure for land fertilization? Do you use it as a source of fuel?
20. Do you use nightsoil for land fertilization?
21. Are there any improvements that you desire in your dwelling?
22. Are there any improvements that you desire in your village?

Questionnaire 3: Information on married women of childbearing age

1. Name, husband's name and birth date
2. Relationship to husband
3. Have you ever been married to someone other than your present husband? If yes, what are the total number of years that you were married?
4. What is the number of male children that you have living with you?
5. What is the number of female children that you have living with you?
6. What is the number of male children that you have living elsewhere?
7. What is the number of female children that you having living elsewhere?
8. How many of your male children were born alive and died?
9. How many of your female children were born alive and died?
10. Have you ever had any miscarriages? If yes, how many?
11. What is the birth date of your last child that was born alive?
12. Is this child still alive?
13. Have you received any prenatal care during pregnancy and what type?
14. Have you received any postnatal care after delivery and what type?
15. Are you pregnant now?
16. If someone consulted you over the issue of contraception, what type would you advise for use?
17. How long have you been married?

Questionnaire 4: Information on children under the age of three years

1. Child's name and date of birth
2. Name of mother and father
3. Birth place of the child
4. Was this child breastfed? Was s/he given powdered milk and at what age? Was s/he given cow or goat's milk and at what age?
5. What are the reasons for giving him/her milk other than mother's milk?
6. When did you begin the introduction of foods other than milk in this child's diet? What kind of food did you give him/her?

7.   When did you completely wean this child off the breast?
8.   Did you face any problems in feeding this child?
9.   Was this child immunised? How many times and by who?
10. Has the child's stool changed colour, consistency or amount
     during the past two weeks? If yes, did s/he have diarrhoea
     and how many times did s/he defecate daily? What did you
     do?
11. In general, what do you think of your child's health?

Questionnaire 5: Information on household migrants

1.   Are there any sons of this household's head who are living
     abroad? How many?
2.   What are their names, ages and occupations?
3.   How long have they been living abroad? Where are they
     currently living?
4.   Are they married? Do they have children? How many?
5.   What is the highest level of education that they have
     achieved?

Questionnaire 6: Information on disease incidence and treatment

1.   Within the last two weeks how many in this household were
     sick and with what?
2.   What was done to treat this sickness?

APPENDIX THREE

THE MCLAREN AND READ CHART FOR
THE ASSESSMENT OF NUTRITIONAL STATUS

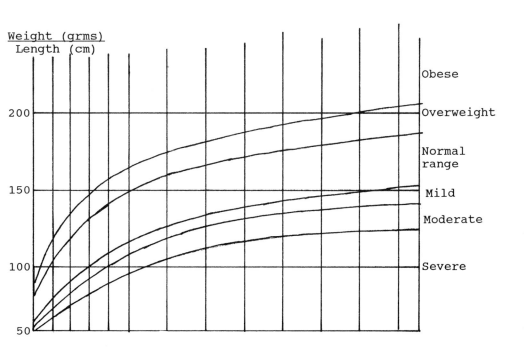

Weight (grms)
Length (cm)

Obese
Overweight
Normal range
Mild
Moderate
Severe

(as % of standard)

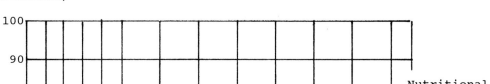

Nutritional dwarf

Age (months)

APPENDIX FOUR

ESTIMATION OF THE LEVEL OF NATURAL FERTILITY FROM REPORTED PARITY BY MARRIAGE DURATION
THE THREE VILLAGES

Table One

Children Ever Born and Ever-Married Women by Time Elapsed Since First Marriage

Marriage duration in years	Duration index (i)	Number of currently married women	Number of ever born children
0-4	1	50	69
5-9	2	61	234
10-14	3	40	223

Table Two

Reported Average Parities by Duration of Marriage

Marriage duration in years	Reported average parities
0-4	1.38
5-9	3.836
10-14	5.575

Table Three

Calculation of Expected Average Parities by Duration of Marriage

Marriage duration	Index (i)	SMAM = 22	SMAM = 23	SMAM = 22.273*
0-4	1	1.137	1.122	1.133
5-9	2	3.324	3.260	3.307
10-14	3	5.278	5.137	5.240

* SMAM (calculated) = 22.273, a_0, the youngest age at which a significant number of women, or 16% of this sample, marry

Table Four

Adjustment Factor by Duration of Marriage

Marriage duration	Adjustment factor $R_{(i)}$
0-4	1.218
5-9	1.156
10-14	1.064
Average R(i)	1.146

Table Five

Adjusted Marital Fertility and Estimated Age Specific Fertility Rates

Age in years	Index (i)	Adjusted marital fertility g(i)	Estimated age-specific fertility f(i)
15-19	1	0.4712	0.0448
20-24	2	0.5379	0.3238
25-29	3	0.5063	0.4443
30-34	4	0.4570	0.4090
35-39	5	0.3697	0.3080
40-44	6	0.1912	0.1782
45-49	7	0.0289	0.0263
Total marital fertility		2.5622	1.7344

Total fertility = 1.7344 x 5 = 8.67

Table Six

Adjusted Birth Rate - Age Specific Fertility Rate f(j) Method

Age in years	Adjusted birth rate (B)
15-19	7.078
20-24	26.8754
25-29	20.4378
30-34	15.542
35-39	16.632
40-44	7.84
45-49	1.157
Total births	95.5

Birth Rate = 0.043

APPENDIX FIVE

ESTIMATION OF CHILD MORTALITY FROM INFORMATION ON CHILDREN EVER BORN AND CHILDREN SURVIVING USING DATA CLASSIFIED BY DURATION OF MARRIAGE

Table One

Average Parities P(i) and Proportions Dead D(i) by Sex of Children and Marriage Duration of Mother

MD*	i	TP	TD	MP	MD	FP	FD	N
0-4	1	1.380	0.101	0.780	0.103	0.600	0.100	51
5-9	2	3.459	0.085	1.721	0.076	1.738	0.094	61
10-14	3	5.575	0.157	3.100	0.153	2.475	0.162	42
15-19	4	7.036	0.173	3.607	0.158	3.429	0.188	25

* MD = marriage duration in years, i = duration index, TP = total parity, TD = total dead, MP = male parity, MD = male dead, FP = female parity, Fd = female dead, N = number of ever married women

Table Two

Trussell's Adjustment Factors by Duration of Marriage

Marriage duration in years	i	Males*	Females	Both sexes
0-4	1	1.1062	1.1725	1.1385
5-9	2	0.9984	1.0177	1.0088
10-14	3	1.0531	0.9995	1.0292
15-19	4	1.0965	1.0069	1.0560

* Male P1/P2 = 0.4532 and P2/P3 = 0.5552, Female P1/P2 = 0.3452 and P2/P3 = 0.7022. For both sexes P1/P2 = 0.3990 and P2/P3 = 0.6205

Table Three

Estimates of q(x) and l(x) obtained by the Trussell Method/
West Model

Marriage duration in years	x	Males q(x)*	Males l(x)	Females q(x)	Females l(x)	Both sexes q(x)	Both sexes l(x)
0-4	2	0.1139	88610	0.1173	88270	0.1150	88500
5-9	3	0.0759	92410	0.0957	90430	0.0858	91420
10-14	5	0.1611	83890	0.1619	83810	0.1616	83840

* q(x) = the probability of dying between birth and exact age x.
  l(x) = the probability of surviving between birth and exact age x.

APPENDIX SIX

EDUCATION LEVEL OF MARRIED WOMEN OF CHILDBEARING AGE BY OTHER PARAMETERS

Table One

Educational Level of Women by their Age

Women's Age in years	Educational levels in years - percentages			Total per cent
	None	1-5	6 or more	
15-19	23	29	48	100
20-29	23	31	46	100
30-39	77	22	1	100
40-49	98	1	1	100

Total women = 264
Chi square: 119.92, $p = 0$

Table Two

Educational Level of Women by the Availability of Latrines in Households

Women's educational level in years	Availability of latrines - percentages			Total per cent
	Inside	Outside	None	
None	9	58	33	100
1-5	10	61	29	100
6 or more	22	59	20	100

Total women = 266

Table Three

Educational Level of Women by Drinking-Water Coverage in their Households

Women's educational level in years	Drinking water coverage - percentages		Total per cent
	Well covered	Not well covered	
None	49	51	100
1-5	61	39	100
6 or more	76	24	100

Total women = 258
Chi square = 13 $p = 0.01$

Table Four

Educational Level of Women by the Receipt of Prenatal Care
During Last Pregnancy

Women's educational level in years	Receipt of prenatal care- percentage of total
None	33
1-5	39
6 or more	71

Total women = 231
Chi square = 12.557   p = 0.005

APPENDIX SEVEN

CHILDREN UNDER THE AGE OF THREE YEARS BY OTHER PARAMETERS

Table One

Children Under the Age of Three Years by Wealth Status
of Household

Number of children under three in years	Wealth status - percentages-		
	High	Medium	Low
1	47	47	24
2	53	45	67
3	0	8	9
Total	100	100	100

Total children = 213

Table Two

Children Under the Age of Three Years by Age of Mother

Number of children under three in years	Age of mother in years - percentages			
	15-19	20-29	30-39	40-49
1	75	33	46	70
2	25	58	47	30
3	0	9	7	0
Total	100	100	100	100

Total children = 212

APPENDIX EIGHT

CHILD MALNUTRITION BY AGE AND SEX

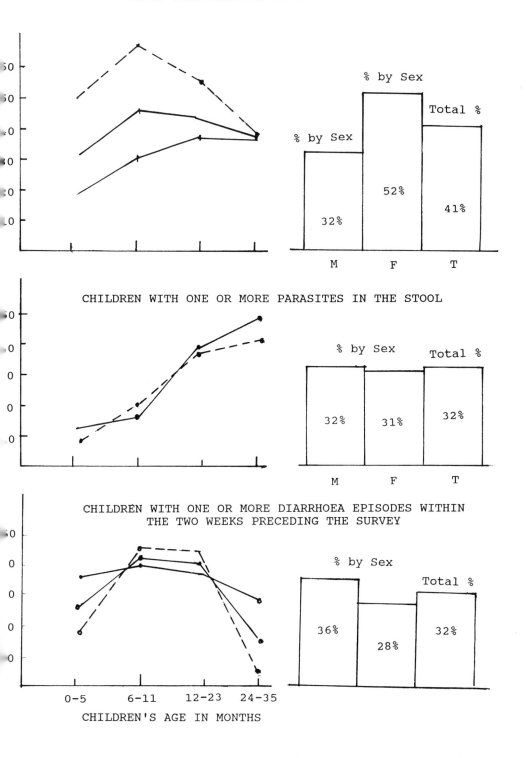

CHILDREN WITH ONE OR MORE PARASITES IN THE STOOL

CHILDREN WITH ONE OR MORE DIARRHOEA EPISODES WITHIN
THE TWO WEEKS PRECEDING THE SURVEY

CHILDREN'S AGE IN MONTHS

APPENDIX NINE

NUTRITIONAL STATUS OF CHILDREN UNDER THE AGE OF THREE YEARS BY OTHER PARAMETERS

Table One

Nutritional Status of Children by the Educational Level of Mothers

Educational level of mothers in years	Nutritional Status of children - percentage Normal	Malnourished	Total per cent
None	58	42	100
1-5	52	48	100
6 or more	65	35	100

Total children = 209

Table Two

Child Malnutrition by Feeding and Weaning Patterns

Child feeding and weaning pattern	Child malnutrition - percentage of feeding and weaning categories Ages 0-35 months	Ages 0-23 months
Breastfed	40	46
Mixed fed breast and powder	42	40
Foods other than milk introduced before the age of 6 months	40	42
Foods other than milk introduced after the age of 6 months	44	46
Weaned on eggs	40	42
Not weaned on eggs	43	44
Weaned on Cerelac (manufactured weaning cereal)	43	44
Not weaned on Cerelac	38	40
Completely weaned off the breast before the age of 6 months	44	40
Completely weaned off the breast after the age of 6 months	38	46

APPENDIX TEN

THE SEX OF CHILDREN UNDER THE AGE OF THREE YEARS
BY OTHER PARAMETERS

Table One

Health and Feeding Behaviour of Mothers by Sex of Children

Health and feeding behaviour of mothers	Sex of children - percentage of sex category	
	Males	Females
Pursued post-natal care for the child	11	6
Only breastfed the child	43	46
Introduced foods other than milk in the child's diet before the age of 6 months	74	68
Weaned the child on Cerelac	58	52
Completely weaned the child before the age of 6 months	52	53

Total Children = 209

Table Two

Child Malnutrition by Sex by Wealth Status of Household

Wealth Status of Household	Child Malnutrition - Percentage of Sex Category	
	Males	Females
High	29	33
Medium and low	38	54

Total children = 211

Table Three

Complete Weaning off the Breast under the Age of Six Months
by Educational Level of Mother and Sex of Child

Educational level of mother in years	Complete weaning off the breast under the age of six months - percentage of sex category	
	Males	Females
None	50	40
1-5	35	60
6 or more	65	72

Total children = 209

APPENDIX ELEVEN

DIARRHOEAL EPISODES IN CHILDREN UNDER THE AGE OF THREE YEARS
BY FEEDING AND WEANING PRACTICES OF THEIR MOTHERS

Feeding and weaning practices of mothers	One or more reported episodes of diarrhoea Percentage of practice category
Breastfed only	31
Mixed fed breast and powdered milk	33
Foods other than milk introduced before the age of six months	35
Foods other than milk introduced after the age of six months	28
Weaned on Cerelac	39
Weaned on home made foods	26
Completely weaned off the breast under the age of six months	33
Completely weaned off the breast after the age of six months	29

BIBLIOGRAPHY

Abolgassem, D et al, 'Assessment of the Nutritional Status of Pre-School Children in Mahabad Rural Areas', Journal of Tropical Pediatrics, Vol. 29, 1983, pp. 329-332.

Abosede, O A, "Self-medication: An Important Aspect of Primary Health Care", Social Science and Medicine, 19/7, 1984.

Agbonifo, P O, "The State of Health as a Reflection of the Level of Development of a Nation", Social Science and Medicine, 17/24, 1983.

Alavi, H and Shanin, T, Introduction to the Sociology of 'Developing Societies', Macmillan, London, 1982.

al-Dabbagh, M, Biladuna Falastin, 2/8, Beirut, 1974 (in Arabic).

Amin, S, Imperialism and Unequal Development, Harvester Press, Sussex, 1977.

Aruri, N, Editor, Occupation Israel Over Palestine, Zed, London, 1984.

Baidoun, A, The Role of Health in Economic Development in the West Bank, Arab Thought Forum, Jerusalem, 1981 .

Barker, D and Rose, G, Epidemiology in Medical Practice, Churchill Livingstone, Edinburgh, 1979.

Barnes, D et al, "Rural Literacy and Agricultural Development: Cause or Effect", Rural Sociology, 47/2, 1982.

Beneson, A S, Editor, Control of Communicable Diseases in Man, American Public Health Association, New York, 1981.

Benvenisti, M, The West Bank and Gaza Data Base Project: A Pilot Study Report, Jerusalem, 1982.

Berg, A, The Nutrition Factor: Its Role in National Development, Brookling Institute, Washington DC, 1973.

Blacker, J G, Hill, A and Moser, K, Mortality Levels and Trends in Jordan Estimated from the Results of the 1976 Fertility Survey, Scientific Reports number 47, International Statistics Institute, Voorburg, Netherlands, 1983.

Blalock, H M, Social Statistics, Second Edition, McGraw-Hill, Tokyo, 1972.

Brown, R and Margo, G E, "Health Eduction: Can the Reformers be Reformed?", International Journal of Health Services, 18/1, 1978.

Budeiri, M, "Changes in the Economic Structure of the West Bank and Gaza Strip Under Israeli Occupation", Labour, Capital and Society, 15/1, 1982.

Bull, D, A Growing Problem: Pesticides and the Third World Poor, Oxfam, Oxford, 1982.

Central Bureau of Statistics, Statistical Abstracts of Israel, Jerusalem, 1981.

Central Bureau of Statistics, Statistical Abstracts of Israel, Jerusalem, 1982.

Chase G D et al, Remington's Pharmaceutical Sciences, Macmillan, Eaton, 1970.

Chojnacka, H and Abegbola, O K, "The Determinants of Infant and Child Morbidity in Lagos, Nigeria", Social Science and Medicine, 19/8, 1984.

Coale, A J and Demeny, P, Regional Model Life Tables and Stable Populations, Princeton University Press, Princeton, 1966.

Colclough, C, "The Impact of Primary Schooling on Economic Development: A Review of the Evidence", World Development, 10/3, 1982.

Constantine, D, "Issues in Community Organization", Community Development Journal, 27/3, 1982.

Crandon, L, "Grass Roots, Herbs, Promoters and Preventions: A Re-evaluation of Contemporary International Health Care Planning, the Bolivian Case", Social Science and Medicine, 17/17, 1983.

Cunningham, A S, "Morbidity in Breast Fed and Artificially Fed Infants", Journal of Pediatrics, 95, 1979.

Davidson, J, "The Survival of Traditional Medicine in a Peruvian Barriada", Social Science and Medicine, 17/17, 1983.

De Castro, J, The Geopolitics of Hunger, Monthly Review, New York, 1977.

De Kadt, E, "Community Participation for Health: The Case of Latin America", World Development, 10/7, 1982.

Dev, K A et al, "Breast Feeding Practices in Urban Slums and Rural Areas of Varansi (India)", Journal of Tropical Pediatrics, 29, 1983.

Djazeyery, A et al, "Assessment of the Nutritional Status of Pre-School Children in Mahabad Rural Areas", Journal of Tropical Pediatrics, 29, 1983.

Doyal, L, The Political Economy of Health, Pluto, London, 1983.

Ebrahim, G J, Breastfeeding: The Biological Option, Macmillan, London 1978.

Ebrahim, G J, Paediatric Practice in Developing Countries, Macmillan, London, 1981.

Ebrahim, G J, Child Health in a Changing Environment, Macmillan, London, 1982.

Edmonston, B and Andes, N, "Community Variations in Infant and Child Mortality in Peru", Journal of Epidemiology and Community Health, 37, 1983.

Ehrenreich, J, Editor, The Cultural Crisis of Modern Medicine, Monthly Review, New York, 1978.

el-Badri, M A, "Higher Female than Male Mortality in Some Countries of South Asia: A Digest", Journal of American Statistical Association, 64, 1969.

Faberga, H, "On the Specificity of Folk Illnesses", South Western Journal of Anthropology, 26, 1970.

Feachem, R et al, Editors, Water, Wastes and Health in Hot Climates, Wiley, Chichester, 1977.

Feder, E, "Plundering the Poor: The Role of the World Bank in the Third World", International Journal of Health Services, 13/4, 1983.

Fee, E, "Women and Health Care: A Comparison of Theories", International Journal of Health Services, 5/3, 1975.

Feuerstein, M T and Lovel, H, Introduction, "Community Development and the Emergence of Primary Health Care", Community Development Journal, 18/2, 1983.

Foster, G, "Anthropological Research Perspectives on Health Problems in Developing Countries", Social Science and Medicine, 18/10, 1984.

Friedson, E, Professions of Medicine, Dood Mead, New York, 1970.

Giacaman, R, "Disturbing Distortions: A Response to the Report of the Ministry of Health of Israel to the Thirty-Sixth World Health Assembly on Health and Health Services in the Occupied Territories, Geneva, May, 1983", Revue d'Etudes Palestiniennes, June 1984.

Graham-Brown, S, Education, Repression, Liberation: Palestinians, World University Service, London, 1984.

Granqvist, H, Marriage Conditions in a Palestinian Village, Helsingfors, 1931.

Granqvist, H, <u>Marriage Conditions in a Palestinian Village</u>, Volume II, Helsingfors, 1935.

Grosse, R, "Inter-Relation Between Health and Population: Observations Derived from Field Experience", <u>Social Science and Medicine</u>, 14C, 1980.

Guerin, V, <u>Description Géographique, Historique et Archéologique de la Palestine: Judée</u>, Tome III, Amsterdam, 1936 (in French).

Hamoud, E and Esmat, I, "Studies in Fetal and Infant Mortality II: Differences in Mortality by Sex and Race", <u>American Journal of Public Health</u>, 55/8, 1965.

<u>Health and Health Services in Judea, Samaria and Gaza: A Report by the Ministry of Health of Israel to the Thirty-Sixth World Health Assembly, Geneva, May, 1983</u>, State of Israel, Ministry of Health, Jerusalem, 1983.

Herbert, D and Hijazi, N, "Ill-health and Health-care in Khartoum/Omdurman", <u>Social Science and Medicine</u>, 18/4, 1984.

Hill, A, "The Palestinian Population of the Middle East", <u>Population and Development Review</u>, 9/2, 1983.

Igun, U A, "Child Feeding Habits in a Situation of Social Change: The Case of Maiduguri, Nigeria", <u>Social Science and Medicine</u>, 16, 1982.

Illich, I, <u>Medical Nemesis: The Expropriation of Health</u>, Pantheon, New York, 1976.

Isliker, H and Schurch, B, <u>The Impact of Malnutrition on Immune Defence in Parasitic Infestation</u>, Hans Huber, Bern, 1981.

<u>Israel Mirror</u>, no. 591, 29/1/82.

<u>Israel Mirror</u>, no. 637, 2/3/83.

<u>Israel Mirror</u>, no. 705-6, 17/10/84.

<u>Israel Mirror</u>, no. 718, 31/1/85.

<u>Israel Mirror</u>, no. 719, 8/2/85.

<u>Israel Mirror</u>, no. 731-32, 20/5/85.

Istfan, F, <u>Materia Medica of the Organic Chemical Substances</u>, American University of Beirut Press, Beirut, 1934.

Jeliffe, D B, <u>The Assessment of the Nutritional Status of the Community</u>, World Health Organization, Geneva, 1966.

Jeliffe, D B and Jeliffe, E P, <u>Human Milk in the Modern World</u>, Oxford University Press, Oxford, 1979.

Katbeh, S, <u>The Status of Health Services in the West Bank</u>, Jordan Medical Council, Jerusalem, 1977.

Kennedy, I, <u>The Unmasking of Medicine</u>, George Allen and Unwin, Boston, 1981.

Knowles, J, "Health, Population and Development", <u>Social Science and Medicine</u>, 14C, 1980.

Koo, L, "The Use of Food to Treat and Prevent Disease in Chinese Culture", <u>Social Science and Medicine</u>, 18/9, 1984.

Laderman, C, "Food Ideology and Eating Behavior: Contributions from Malay Studies", <u>Social Science and Medicine</u>, 19/5, 1984.

Leigh, J P, "Direct and Indirect Effects of Education on Health", <u>Social Science and Medicine</u>, 17/4, 1983.

Levinson, S and Mcfate, R, <u>Clinical Laboratory Diagnosis</u>, Lea and Febiger, Philadelphia, 1969.

Makhoul, N, "Assessment and Implementation of Health Care Priorities: Incompatible Paradigms and Competing Social Systems", <u>Social Science and Medicine</u>, 19/4, 1984.

Manderson, L, "These are Modern Times: Infant Feeding Practices in Peninsular Malaysia", <u>Social Science and Medicine</u>, 18/1, 1983.

Ma'oz, M, <u>Palestinian Leadership on the West Bank</u>, Frank Cass, London, 1984.

Mara, D and Feachem, R, "Technical and Public Health Aspects of Low Cost Sanitation Programme Planning", <u>Journal of Tropical Medicine and Hygiene</u>, 83, 1980.

Marcus, A, Seeman, T and Telesky, C, "Sex Differences in Reports of Illness and Disability: A Further Test of the Fixed Role Hypothesis", <u>Social Science and Medicine</u>, 17/15, 1983.

Marshall, L and Marshall, M, "Infant Feeding and Infant Illness in a Micronesian Village", <u>Social Science and Medicine</u>, 14B, 1980.

Martin, W and Beittel, M, <u>The Hidden Abode of Reproduction: Conceptualizing Households in Southern Africa</u>, Research Working Group Papers, Fernand Braudel Center for the Study of Economies, Historical Systems and Civilizations, State University of New York at Binghamton, New York, 1984.

Mata, L, <u>The Children of Santa Marra Cauque: A Prospective Field Study of Health and Growth</u>, MIT Press, Cambridge, 1978.

Mckeown, T, <u>The Modern Rise of Population</u>, Arnold, London, 1976.

Mckeown, T, <u>The Role of Medicine: Dream, Mirage or Nemesis</u>, Blackwell, Oxford, 1979.

Mclaren, D S and Read, W, "Weight/Length Classification of Nutritional Status", <u>The Lancet</u>, August, 1975.

Meillasoux, C, "The Economic Bases of Demographic Reproduction: From the Domestic Mode of Production to Wage-Earning", <u>Journal of Peasant Studies</u>, 11/1, 1983.

Meldrum, B and DiDomenico, C, "Production and Reproduction. Women and Breastfeeding: Some Nigerian Examples", <u>Social Science and Medicine</u>, 16, 1982.

Melrose, D, <u>Bitter Pills: Medicines and the Third World Poor</u>, Oxfam, Oxford, 1982.

Morrison, D E and Henkel, R E, <u>The Significance Test Controversy</u>, Butterworths, London, 1970.

Morsay, S, "Towards a Political Economy of Health: A Critical Note on the Medical Anthropology of the Middle East", <u>Social Science and Medicine</u>, 15B, 1981.

Muir Gray, J and Fowler, G, <u>Essentials in Preventive Medicine</u>, Blackwell, Oxford, 1984.

Nadarjah, T, "The Transition From Higher Female to Higher Male Mortality in Sri Lanka", <u>Population and Development Review</u>, 9/2, 1983.

Nakhleh, K and Zureik, E, Editors, <u>The Sociology of the Palestinians</u>, Croom Helm, London, 1980.

Naphanson, C, "Sex, Illness and Medical Care: A Review of Data, Theory and Method", <u>Social Science and Medicine</u>, 2, 1980.

Navarro, V, Editor, <u>Imperialism, Health and Medicine</u>, Pluto, London, 1982.

Navarro, V, <u>Medicine Under Capitalism</u>, Croom Helm, London, 1982.

Nie, N H et al, <u>Statistical Package for the Social Sciences</u>, McGraw   Hill, New York, 1975.

Oswald, I H, "Are Traditional Healers the Solution to the Failure of Primary Health Care in Rural Nepal?", <u>Social Science and Medicine</u>, 17/5, 1983.

Owen, R, Editor, <u>Studies in the Economic and Social History of Palestine in the Nineteenth and Twentieth Centuries</u>, Macmillan, London, 1982.

Patti, M et al, "Episodes of Illness in Breastfed and Bottlefed Infants in Jerusalem", <u>Israel Journal of Medical Science</u>, 20/5, 1984.

Pederson, D and Coloma, C, "Traditional Medicine in Ecuador: The Structure of the Non-Formal Health System", <u>Social Science and Medicine</u>, 17/17, 1983.

Popkin, B and Lim-Ybanez, M, "Nutrition and School Achievement", <u>Social Science and Medicine</u>, 16, 1982.

Pridham, B R, Editor, <u>Economy, Society and Culture in Contemporary Yemen</u>, Croom Helm, Kent, 1985.

Puyet, J H, <u>Infant Mortality Studies Conducted Among Selected Refugee Camp Communities in the Near East</u>, United Nations Relief and Works Agency, Vienna, 1979.

Rehan, N, "Knowledge, Attitude and Practice of Family Planning in Hausa Women", <u>Social Science and Medicine</u>, 18/10, 1984.

Reidy, A, "Marxist Functionalism in Medicine: A Critique of the Work of Vicente Navarro on Health and Medicine", <u>Social Science and Medicine</u>, 19/9, 1984.

Riaz, A P and Shahid, I R, "Incidence of Intestinal Protozoan Parasites of Man in the Twin Cities of Rawalpindi-Islamabad", <u>Journal of Pakistani Medical Association</u>, July, 1983.

Roberts, A, Jorgensen, B and Newman, F, <u>Academic Freedom under Israeli Military Occupation: Report of WUS/ICJ Mission of Inquiry into Higher Education in the West Bank and Gaza</u>, World University Service/International Commission of Jurists, London/Geneva, 1984.

Robertson, J S, and Sheard, A V, "Altered Sex Ratio After an Outbreak of Hepatitis", <u>The Lancet</u>, 1, 1973.

Robinson, D, <u>Patients, Practitioners and Medical Care: Aspects of Medical Sociology</u>, Heineman, London, 1983.

Rodinson, M, <u>Israel: A Colonial Settler State</u>? Mondad, New York, 1973.

Rosenfield, P, Golladary, F and Davidson, R K, "The Economics of Parasitic Disease: Research Priorities", <u>Social Science and Medicine</u>, 19/10, 1984.

Rothschild, J, Editor, <u>Forbidden Agendas: Intolerance and Defiance in the Middle East</u>, al-Saqi, London, 1984.

Roxborough, I, <u>Theories of Underdevelopment</u>, Macmillan, London, 1979.

Sadler, P G and Abu-Kishk, B, <u>Palestine: Options for Development</u>, United Nations Conference on Trade and Development, Trade and Development Board, Twenty-Seventh Session Geneva, October, 1983.

Said, E, The Question of Palestine, Routledge and Kegan Paul, London, 1980.

Salus: Low-Cost Rural Health Care and Health Manpower Training, International Development Research Centre, Ottawa, vol 13, 1984.

Sayigh, R, "Encounters with Palestinian Women Under Occupation", Journal of Palestine Studies, 10/4, 1981.

Schmeltz, O U, Nathan, G and Kenvin, J, Multiplicity Study of Births and Deaths in Judea, Samaria and Gaza Strip, North Sinai, Technical Publication Series no. 44, Israel Central Bureau of Statistics, Jerusalem, 1977.

Schoefield, S, Development and the Problems of Village Nutrition, Croom Helm, London, 1979.

Schoelch, A, Editor, Palestinians Over the Green Line, Ithaca, London, 1983.

Shear Wood, C, "Early Childhood: The Critical Stage in Human Interaction with Disease and Culture", Social Science and Medicine, 19/5, 1984.

Shehadeh, R and Kuttab, J, The West Bank and the Rule of Law, International Commission of Jurists / Law in the Service of Man, New York, 1980.

Simmonds, S, Vaughan, P and Gunn, S W, Refugee Community Health Care, Oxford University Press, 1983.

Somers, A and Somers, H, Health and Health Care in Perspective, Aspen Systems Corporation, Maryland, 1977.

Strong, P M, "Sociological Imperialism and the Profession of Medicine: A Critical Examination of the Thesis of Medical Imperialism", Social Science and Medicine, 13A, 1979.

Suarez, M, "Etiology, Hunger and Folk Diseases in the Venezuelan Andes", Journal of Anthropological Research, 30, 1974.

Susser, M W and Watson, W, Sociology in Medicine, Oxford University Press, London, 1971.

Tabari, A and Yeganeh, N, In the Shadow of Islam: The Women's Movement in Iran, Zed, London, 1982.

Tamari, S and Giacaman, R, The Social Impact of Drip Irrigation on a Palestinian Peasant Community in the Jordan Valley, Birzeit University, Birzeit, 1980.

Tamari, S, "Building Other People's Homes: The Palestinian Peasant's Household and Work in Israel", Journal of Palestine Studies, 11/1, 1981

Bibliography

185

Tillion, G, The Republic of Cousins, al-Saqi, London, 1983.

Turshen, M and Thebaud, A, "International Medical Aid", Monthly Review, 33, 1981.

United Nations, Economic Activity and Access to National Resources: Legal Restrictions on Access to Land and Water in Israel, Document A/CONF.114/6, 20 June, 1983.

United Nations, Manual X: Indirect Techniques for Demographic Estimation, New York, 1983.

Van Arkadie, B, Benefits and Burdens: A Report on the West Bank and Gaza Strip Economy Since 1967, Carnegie Endowment for International Peace, New York, 1977.

Waitzkin, H, "The Social Origins of Illness: A Neglected History", International Journal of Health Services, 11/1, 1981.

Waldron, E, "Sex Differences in Human Mortality: The Role of the Genetic Factor", Social Science and Medicine, 17/6, 1983

Waldron, E, "Sex Differences in Illness Incidence, Prognosis and Mortality: Issues and Evidence", Social Science and Medicine, 17/16, 1983.

Warren, B, Imperialism Pioneer of Capitalism, Verso, London, 1980.

Waseem, M, "Local Power Structures and the Relevance of Rural Development Strategies: A Case Study from Pakistan", Community Development Journal, 17/3, 1982.

Washburn, T and Medearis, D, "Sex Differences in Susceptibility to Infection", Pediatrics, January, 1965.

Winikoff, B and Brown, G, "Nutrition, Population and Health: Theoretical and Practical Issues", Social Science and Medicine, 14C, 1980.

Winthrope, M et al, Editors, Harrison's Principles of Internal Medicine, McGraw Hill, New York, 1974.

Wood, C, "The Political Economy of Child Mortality in Sao Paolo, Brazil", International Journal of Health Services, 12/2, 1982.

World Health Organization, Alma-Ata Declaration, 1978.

World Health Organization, Manual of Basic Techniques for a Health Laboratory, Geneva, 1980.

World Health Organization, Thirty-Fourth World Health Assembly, Summary Records of Committees, Document WHA. 34/181/REC/3, 4-22 May, 1981.

World Health Organization, <u>Health Conditions of the Arab</u>
<u>Population in the Occupied Arab Territories, Including</u>
<u>Palestine</u>, Report of the Special Committee of Experts Appointed
to Study the Health Conditions of the Inhabitants of the
Occupied Territories, Document A36/14, 28 April, 1983.

Wright, P and Treacher, A, Editors, <u>The Problem of Medical</u>
<u>Knowledge: Examining the Social Construction of Medicine</u>,
Edinburgh University Press, Edinburgh, 1982.

Wylie, Robert, "Effutu Curing: Preliminary Survey of Traditional
and Spiritual Healers", <u>Current Anthropology</u>, 24/3, 1983.

Zureik, E, <u>The Palestinians in Israel: A Study in Internal</u>
<u>Colonialism</u>, Routledge and Kegan Paul, London, 1979.

<u>Unpublished Reports and Documents</u>

<u>Bulletin of Palestinian Working Women's Union in the West Bank</u>
<u>and Gaza Strip</u>, Jerusalem, August, 1983.

Catholic Relief Services, <u>Health Education Project, Historical</u>
<u>Background and Annual Report</u>, January 1, 1982 - December 31,
1982.

Giacaman, R, <u>Planning for Health in Occupied Palestine</u>, Birzeit
University, Birzeit, 1982.

Giacaman, R, <u>Palestinian Women and Development in the Occupied</u>
<u>West Bank</u>, Paper Presented at the 7th United Nations' Seminar
on the Question of Palestine, Dakkar, Senegal, August, 1983.

Giacaman, R, <u>Community Development in the Israeli Occupied West</u>
<u>Bank: A Case Study in Health Promotion</u>, Birzeit University,
Birzeit, 1983.

Giacaman, R, <u>The Raymah Health Project: An Evaluation</u>, Oxfam,
Oxford, 1984.

Landrigan, P J and Miller, B, <u>Epidemic of Acute Illness in the</u>
<u>West Bank</u>, Center for Disease Control, Atlanta, 1983.

Myntti, C, <u>Health and Healing in Rural North Yemen</u>, Cairo, 1985.

Union of Palestinian Medical Relief Committees, <u>Statement of</u>
<u>Purpose and Activities</u>, Jerusalem, 1983.

Union of Palestinian Medical Relief Committees, <u>Light on Medical</u>
<u>Problems in the West Bank</u>, Jerusalem, 1984.

Voluntary Work Committees for the West Bank and Gaza, <u>Statement</u>
<u>of Purpose and Activities</u> (not dated).

Women's Work Committees in the Occupied Territories, <u>Towards Building a United Women's Movement in the Occupied Territories</u>, Report to the Second General Conference of the Women's Work Committee in the Occupied Territories, March, 1983.

Women's Work Committees in the Occupied Territories, Bulletin December 1983, January/February 1984.